# THE WAY SCIENCE WORKS

By
Robin Kerrod and
Dr. Sharon Ann Holgate

A DORLING KINDERSLEY BOOK
In association with the Science Museum, London

Dorling **DK** Kindersley

LONDON, NEW YORK, MUNICH,
MELBOURNE, and DELHI

**Project editors** Kate Bradshaw, Maggie Crowley,
Caryn Jenner, Amanda Rayner, Sadie Smith
**Art editors** Sheila Collins, Guy Harvey,
Joanna Pocock, Wilfred Wood
**Senior editor** Kitty Blount
**Senior art editor** Martin Wilson
**Category publisher** Jayne Parsons
**Managing art editor** Jacquie Gulliver
**Art director** Cathy Tincknell
**Picture research** Marie Osborn, Sarah Pownall
**Picture librarians** Sally Hamilton,
Rose Horridge, Sarah Mills
**Jacket design** Dean Price
**DTP designer** Siu Yin Ho
**Production controller** Erica Rosen
**Special photography** Trish Gant
**Digital artwork** Robin Hunter, John Kelly
**Science experiments advisor** David Phillips

First published in hardback in Great Britain in 2002
This paperback edition first published in 2008
by Dorling Kindersley Limited,
80 Strand, London WC2R 0RL

Copyright © 2002 Dorling Kindersley Limited
A Penguin Company

2  4  6  8  10 (HB) 9  7  5  3  1
2  4  6  8  10 (PB) 9  7  5  3  1
TD083 – 03/08

A CIP catalogue record for this book is
available from the British Library.

Hardback ISBN: 978-0-75133-981-9
Paperback ISBN: 978-1-40533-193-7

Colour reproduction by Colourscan, Singapore
Printed and bound by Toppan, China

**Discover more at**
**www.dk.com**

# CONTENTS

## ATOMS AND ELEMENTS 38–59

# THE WAY SCIENCE WORKS

**SCIENTISTS CAN MAKE MOLECULES THE SIZE OF** pollen grains that whiz around like propellers. They can do this by using devices that can pick up and move individual atoms. Using chemical "scissors", they can cut and splice genes and transfer them from one living organism to another. They can make electricity from sunlight, peer into the brain, and probe deep into space to unravel the secrets of the Universe. However, science is not just about the amazing and the fantastic. There is science behind everything that happens in our world – when a ball falls, or a rocket takes off; when lightning flashes and thunder booms; when birds fly and fish swim; when water freezes and lava flows; and when a match burns.

## THE BIG THREE

Let us examine the science behind a match. When you strike the match, the muscles in your fingers produce a force that pulls the match over a rough surface. The friction between the match head and the rough surface produces heat energy, triggering a chemical reaction in the head that gives out more energy as heat and light. If you let the match burn down, it will burn you. Nerve endings in your fingers will send messages to your brain to say "pain" and force your fingers to release the burned match. All three main sciences are involved in striking the match – physics, chemistry, and human biology. Physics is the study of energy, forces, and matter. It has many branches. For example, in nuclear physics, scientists investigate the forces and energy within the nuclei (centres) of atoms. Chemistry

## EXPERIMENTS – SAFETY FIRST

Before conducting any experiment, be sure to read it carefully. Think of the things that could go wrong first, and be prepared. You should consider whether the experiment could injure yourself or somebody else. This is called risk assessment. Here are a list of things that must be considered before conducting any kind of scientific experiment:

### General points to remember
• Tell an adult immediately if you have an accident of any kind. Do not attempt to clean up any breakages yourself.
• Always follow instructions carefully. Ask if you are unsure.
• Do not use chemicals or equipment unless you have permission.
• Wear eye protection when necessary

### Heating
• When heating anything, always wear safety goggles and tie back long hair and loose clothing.
• If heating liquids in a test tube, always hold it correctly – use tongs and point away from yourself and anyone else. Never look directly down a heated test tube.
• If you need to pick up hot equipment use tongs and/or heatproof gloves. Allow equipment to cool before putting it away.
• Always have a fire extinguisher or fire blanket on hand in case of an accident. If burned, hold the burn under cool running water and tell an adult.

*Breaking surface tension with detergent*

### Using chemicals
• Never put chemicals in or near your mouth.
• Always wash your hands after experimenting with chemicals. If chemicals get on your skin or in your eyes, wash immediately with water only and tell an adult.

### Electrical equipment
• **NEVER EXPERIMENT WITH MAINS ELECTRICITY.**
• If using electrical equipment, other than battery powered, ensure that the equipment is not near water. Never touch electrical equipment with wet hands.
• Never dismantle electrical equipment.

## SAFE SCIENCE

In this book symbols are used to indicate whether an experiment is safe to do at home with adult supervision, or should be demonstrated in a school laboratory. If an experiment has no symbol at all, it is safe to do on your own. However, always tell an adult first.

*Testing for acidity*

### LET'S EXPERIMENT
THE LAWS OF REFLECTION

 **Adult supervision**
Experiments shown with this symbol must only be done with the help of an adult.

### DEMONSTRATING
MELTING POINTS

**Laboratory experiments**
You must not attempt to do these experiments at home. Ask an adult, such as your science teacher, to demonstrate them in a laboratory for you.

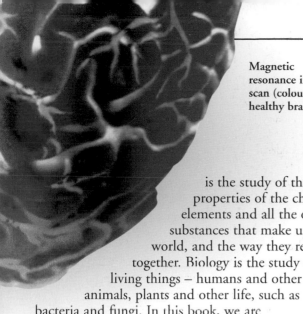

Magnetic resonance imaging scan (coloured) of healthy brain

is the study of the properties of the chemical elements and all the other substances that make up our world, and the way they react together. Biology is the study of living things – humans and other animals, plants and other life, such as bacteria and fungi. In this book, we are concerned mainly with the physical sciences – physics and chemistry.

## SCIENTIFIC METHOD

Strictly speaking, the word science means knowledge. We think of it in particular as knowledge about the world around us – what it's like, how it changes, and what makes it tick. Scientists go about getting this knowledge in a special way, which hinges on two key features – observation and experiment. They see something happen and carefully take note. Then they put forward a possible idea, or theory, that might explain their observations. The next stage is to devise a series of experiments to back up their idea. The results from the experiments may be favourable, in which case the scientists may be able to convert their idea into a law. If the results are unfavourable, they will be forced to try other ideas and other experiments. Along the way, the scientists may come across all kinds of interesting things they didn't know before. William Henry Perkin discovered one of the first synthetic dyes, mauveine, while he was trying to make artificial quinine. When they were researching uranium radiation, Marie and Pierre Curie found a new radioactive element, which they called polonium.

Home-built rocket blasts off, propelled by water jet.

## DO-IT-YOURSELF

You will be following in the footsteps of great scientists when you carry out the experiments in this book. Like those scientists, you can gain knowledge by observation and experiment. Before starting an experiment, read the instructions carefully. Ask an adult for explanation if you don't understand what to do. Take your time to think about what you are doing. If the experiment doesn't work first time, double check you have done everything properly. In electrical experiments, for example, check that all the connecting wires are making contact. Keep an experiment notebook and record the date of your experiment, what you did, what you observed, and note down any results. In some experiments, for example, with a swinging pendulum, you will need to compare your results to work out the basic laws of the pendulum.

Light-bulb filament glows white-hot.

## AT THE CUTTING EDGE

As you read through the book and carry out the experiments, you will realize that science is one of the most fascinating subjects there is. Scarcely a day goes by without the announcement of new scientific advances. In the years ahead, you could be in the forefront of the continuing revolution that is science. You could be creating new drugs to combat cancer; building intelligent robots that could think for themselves; or designing nuclear fusion reactors that could give the world energy forever. You could even be among the first scientist-astronauts to set foot on Mars and hunt for fossils of ancient Martian life.

### Cross-reference boxes

Boxes like this occur on some of the pages. They cover an aspect of the particular science discussed but also relate to the science on another page. For example, this box (right) on radio telescopes appears on page 147 and cross-refers you to page 112, which discusses telescopes.

### ◂ TUNING IN ▸

In 1932, a US electrical engineer named Karl Jansky detected radio waves coming from space, and launched radio astronomy. Astronomers pick up radio waves from space with huge, dish-shaped radio telescopes. Their study of the radio universe led to the discovery of new astronomical bodies, such as quasars, pulsars, and radio galaxies. **113** ▸

*Parkes radio telescope in New South Wales, Australia, has a dish 64 m (210 ft) across.*

# LOOKING AT MATTER

**Picture:** *Liquid crystal photographed in polarised light through an optical microscope.*

# STATES OF MATTER

**EVERYTHING AROUND US IS MADE FROM MATTER,** including our own bodies. Matter is made from atoms and the amount of matter in an object is known as its mass. The most common types or "states" of matter are solids, liquids, and gases. However there are other states of matter, including plasmas, that can form at either extremely high or extremely low temperatures. Under certain conditions, matter can change from one state to another. When solids melt, for example, they turn into liquids, and when liquids boil, they become gases.

## SOLIDS

Atoms and molecules in solids can't move around like those in liquids and gases. This means you can pick up solids, whereas liquids just slip through your hands. The arrangement of atoms in a solid can either be crystalline or amorphous. If crystalline, a particular pattern of atoms is regularly repeated. If amorphous, the atoms are arranged much more randomly.

*This rock and the yellow diamond embedded in it are both solids.*

*If liquids, such as this cranberry juice, are poured quickly, they can produce enough force to knock over a glass.*

## LIQUIDS

The structure of a liquid is halfway between the structure of a solid and that of a gas. Unlike solids, which remain the same shape if they are put into a container, liquids flow to take the shape of whatever is holding them. Their atoms and molecules can move about more than in a solid, but not as much as in a gas. They can slide past one another, so a liquid can flow. Some molecules find it harder to slide along and the liquids made from these don't flow as easily; they are said to have a high viscosity.

## GASES

The molecules in a gas are further apart and move even more freely than those in a liquid. They behave as though they are completely separate, which means gases have no structure, and expand to fill whatever space is available to them. However, the atoms do come into contact with one another, since they constantly move around hitting into each other. Most gases are invisible. Even steam from a kettle can't be seen until it condenses into a mist of liquid droplets. But some gases can be detected by their smell.

*Nitrogen dioxide gas is being produced by a chemical reaction.*

## CHANGING STATE

If a solid is heated to a particular temperature, known as its melting point, it changes into a liquid. If a liquid is heated to its boiling point it turns into a gas. These changes from one type of matter to another are known as changes of state. Cooling has a similar effect, condensing gases into liquids and freezing liquids into solids. Different substances have different melting and boiling points. The temperatures of these points change when the surrounding pressure changes, or when another substance is added. Decreased pressure lowers the boiling point of water, so at the top of Mount Everest water boils at 82°C (180°F) instead of 100°C (212°F). By contrast, adding salt raises the boiling point of water, so salted water boils at a hotter temperature than pure water.

## PLASMA

As well as the familiar states of matter of solid, liquid, and gas, there are also some more unfamiliar states like plasma. Plasma is a special type of gas made from parts of atoms. Plasmas form either when a

c 265 BC Greek mathematician Archimedes discovers relative density.

1644 Italian physicist Evangelista Torricelli constructs the first barometer.

1662 Irish scientist Robert Boyle makes the link between a gas's pressure and volume.

1738 Swiss mathematician Daniel Bernoulli describes liquid and gas movement.

1774 English chemist Joseph Priestley produces oxygen.

1781 French mineralogist René Just Haüy discovers the internal shape of crystals.

*Electricity has created streams of plasma from the gas inside this plasma ball.*

gas is heated to an extremely high temperature, or when an electric current is passed through it. In both cases, this causes electrons to be separated from their atoms. The Sun makes plasma naturally, but scientists are currently experimenting with artificially created plasmas to see if they can be used to help generate electricity in the power stations of the future.

## ANTIMATTER

The Universe is made from matter, but modern experiments suggest that when the Universe was created in the Big Bang, equal amounts of matter and antimatter were formed. Antimatter is like a mirror image of matter. Every particle of matter has a corresponding particle of antimatter, and when they meet they annihilate each other. No-one knows how we are living in a Universe made entirely of matter, since the equal amounts of matter and antimatter originally created should have destroyed each other. By investigating antimatter, created in special experiments, scientists hope to work out the answer and discover how the Universe exists.

## DARK MATTER

Around 90 per cent of the Universe could be made from a mysterious type of matter known as dark matter. Scientists do not yet know what dark matter is made from, but it could contain new types of particles that have not yet been discovered. Dark matter cannot be seen or detected directly, but scientists believe it is there because of the effect it seems to be having on matter that we can see.

*Antimatter can be created in particle physics experiments. This picture shows the tracks made by electrons (green) and positrons (red). Positrons are the antiparticles of electrons.*

*Erupting volcanoes throw out molten rock in the form of liquid lava. The lava in this picture is flowing into the sea, which is cooling it. When lava becomes cool enough, it changes state and becomes solid rock.*

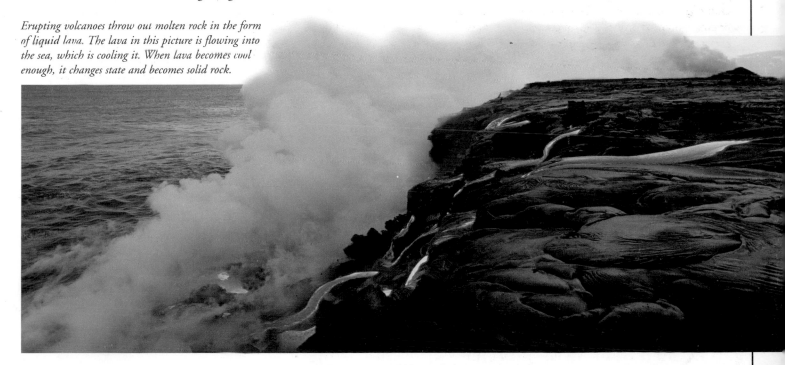

**1783** French chemist Antoine Lavoisier explains that water is composed of hydrogen and oxygen.

**1787** French physicist and chemist Jacques Charles links a gas's temperature and volume.

**1812** German mineralogist Friedrich Mohs defines hardness scale.

**1912** German physicist Max von Laue invents X-ray crystallography.

**1928** English theoretical physicist Paul Dirac predicts antimatter existence.

**1932** American physicist Carl Anderson detects antimatter.

# PROPERTIES OF MATTER

**DIFFERENT TYPES OF MATTER CAN BE IDENTIFIED** by their different properties. The main mechanical properties of matter include hardness, density, strength, and elasticity. Some of these properties are only possessed by certain states of matter – solids can have elasticity, but liquids and gases cannot. However other properties, such as density, are common to all states of matter. Different substances have very different values of these various properties, for example air can be about 1,000 times less dense than water. Manufacturers use standard tests for different properties when they develop new materials to help them understand how they will behave.

*This over-stretched spring can no longer return to its original shape.*

*Bar of chocolate*  
*Plastic ruler*  
*Candle wax*  
*Metal ruler*  
*Wooden spatula*

*Each substance is used to test the comparative hardness of the others.*

## HARDNESS

A solid's resistance to being dented or scratched is known as its hardness. The hardest natural substance is diamond. Diamonds can scratch into all other solids – and other diamonds – so are often used in industry for cutting. This picture (left) shows how scratching can be used to compare hardness. Five substances were pressed into modelling clay, and then the same substances were used to scratch them. The metal ruler could scratch everything, whereas the chocolate was only able to scratch itself (and the modelling clay). Which was the hardest substance used?

## STRENGTH

The amount of force, or stress, that a material can withstand before it crushes or breaks is known as its strength. Strength varies widely. The strength of some materials varies depending on what type of stress is applied to them. Concrete is strong when compressed, but much weaker when stretched. The concrete pillars supporting this fly-over in the USA are compressed by the weight of the road above them.

## Elasticity

If a solid object or material returns to its original shape and size after it has been stretched, we say is it elastic. If the force used to stretch any material is larger than its "elastic limit", the object will be left permanently stretched. This metal spring has been stretched beyond its elastic limit.

**DENSITY IS THE** amount of matter contained in a specific volume. A block of wood is less dense than a block of iron the same size. This experiment shows how to work out the density of an object. **You will need**: an adult to help you; kitchen scales; plastic drinks bottle; plastic straw; modelling clay; measuring jug; solid objects for testing.

**1** Use the scales to weigh each object to be tested. This value is the mass. Mass is the amount of matter in an object, while weight is the force exerted on it by gravity. Weight changes as gravity changes – in space for example – but mass remains constant.

**2** Ask an adult to cut off the top of the bottle and make a hole in the side of the bottle near the top edge. Make a spout by fixing the straw into the hole with clay. The clay seals the edge, making it watertight.

**3** Place the measuring jug below the spout, then fill the bottle with water. The spout keeps an even water level in the bottle by letting any extra water drip out. Empty the excess water from the measuring jug.

**4** Place the object to be tested into the water and watch as the water shoots down the spout. Measure the amount of water displaced into the jug. This is the object's volume. To obtain its density, divide the mass of the object by its volume.

## Brittleness

When certain solids such as the boiled sweets shown above are hit, they shatter. They are termed brittle because they hardly bend or squash before they break. By contrast, ductile materials are much softer and tend to deform before breaking. A china tea cup will smash when dropped because it is brittle, but a metal automobile body is ductile and tends to deform when hit.

*Memory metal spectacles being twisted.*

## Smart materials

Materials that can react cleverly to changes in their surroundings are called "smart" materials. These memory metal spectacle frames will return to their original shape even after being bent. There are many different types of smart materials. Some have sensors embedded in them that can warn engineers they are about to break. Others can change their properties under different circumstances.

# SOLIDS

**THE ATOMS IN SOLIDS VIBRATE LESS THAN THE ATOMS IN** liquids or gases. This means that the atoms in solids remain in the same place, so solids stay the same size and shape. Heating a solid to its melting point causes the order of the atoms to break down. The result is that the solid melts and becomes a liquid. There are many different types of solids. They range from rocks, metals, and plastics, through bricks and concrete, to nylon and rubber. All of these solids have very different values of properties, such as hardness, strength, and elasticity. The type of order of the atoms gives a solid some of its properties.

*A rock climber scales the vertical face of a cliff. Most of the Earth is made from solid rock.*

## METALS

Metals have a vast range of uses. They are sometimes used inside the human body. The lilac shape (right) is an artificial hip joint made from metal. Most elements are metals. Metals look shiny and are good conductors of electricity and heat. We tend to think of them as being very hard, but in fact pure metals are often quite soft and can easily be hammered or pulled into different shapes. Some rare metals like gold can be found on their own, but most are found combined with other elements, in rocks called ores. Melting is used to separate these metals from the other elements.

*This bicycle frame is made from chrome molybdenum, a steel alloy.*

### Alloys
Mixtures of metals, such as bronze made from copper and tin, or mixtures of metals and non-metallic elements, such as steel made from iron and carbon, are known as alloys. Alloys mix together different substances to combine their properties. They can therefore be tailor-made for specific applications.

## ‹ POLYMERS ›

Some solids can be artificially created. Polymers, which are made up from long chains of molecules, are either natural such as rubber, or artificially made such as plastics and nylon. We use a lot of polymers everyday. Food and drinks containers, and many household objects are made from plastic. 56 ▶

**Composites**
Solid materials that are made by combining substances with different useful properties, are known as composites. Reinforced concrete (shown in the picture) is a building material that has steel rods embedded in it to make it much stronger when it is under tension.

# MELTING

The atoms in solids vibrate all the time, but when solids are heated they vibrate much more. If the solid is hot enough, the atoms or molecules move about so much that they can't stay in one place any more. At this temperature, known as the melting point, the solid becomes a liquid. The heat from this flame (right) has turned the wax into a liquid. Different substances have different melting points. For example, ice melts at 0°C (32°F), while gold melts at 1,065°C (1,949°F).

## DEMONSTRATING MELTING POINTS

**DIFFERENT SOLIDS** melt at different temperatures. Scientists use this method to measure melting points. As the water and melting substances will be very hot, this demonstration must be done by an adult in a science lab. **The demonstrator will need**: beaker of water; test tube; tongs; heat source; chocolate, butter, and candle wax to melt; thermometer that goes up to 100°C (212°F).

**1** Each substance is tested separately. The demonstrator puts one substance into the test tube, and places it in a beaker of water (heat bath). The demonstrator slowly heats the beaker, while gently stirring the water to ensure even heating. As the substance starts to melt, the demonstrator removes the test tube from the water.

**2** The demonstrator immediately measures the temperature of the water to obtain the melting point of each substance.

## LET'S EXPERIMENT
### ICE CUTTING

**NORMALLY, ICE** stays frozen below 0°C (32°F), but pressure can cause it to melt. For example, there is often a thin layer of water under glaciers due to pressure melting. You can observe the effects of pressure on ice in this experiment. **You will need**: an ice cube; a bottle; a copper wire; two weights.

**1** Tie the weights to either end of the copper wire. Place the ice cube on top of the open bottle and hang the weighted wire over the top of the ice cube.

**2** Pressure from the wire melts the ice below it, allowing the wire to pass through the ice cube. As the wire drops, the water above it re-freezes because it is no longer under pressure.

# CRYSTALS

**MANY SOLIDS ARE CRYSTALLINE – THIS MEANS THAT**
their atoms are arranged in a repeated pattern. If a crystal
is particularly well formed, it will reveal this regular
internal pattern by its outward shape.
Crystals are often brightly coloured,
and we use some as gemstones,
particularly rare and beautiful
types like diamond and
emerald. Not all crystalline
substances look like
crystals, though. Rocks
are made from minerals,
most of which are
crystalline, and solid
metals can be crystalline,
too. There are even tiny
crystals inside our bodies.
Bones contain crystals of a
mineral called apatite, and
our inner ears contain tiny
crystals which help us to
know which way is up.

### X-ray crystallography
To learn more about crystals, scientists need
to know how the atoms are arranged inside.
They often use a technique called X-ray
crystallography, which was invented in 1912
by the German physicist Max von Laue.
This involves shooting X-rays at a
crystal and analysing the patterns
produced on photographic
film as the atoms scatter the
X-rays. The arrangement
of atoms inside each
type of crystal is
different and shows
up as a different
pattern. In 1953,
this method was
used to reveal
the structure
of the DNA
molecule.

*X-ray diffraction
pattern obtained from
a crystal of the plant
enzyme, Rubisco.*

## CRYSTAL FORMATIONS
Every type of crystal has its atoms arranged in a particular pattern
that repeats over and over to form the whole solid. The patterns,
and numbers of atoms in them, differ depending on the crystalline
substance. However, there are only seven basic geometric shapes –
known as crystal systems – that these patterns can have. The
shapes are cubic, orthorhombic, hexagonal, tetragonal, trigonal,
monoclinic, and triclinic. The crystals pictured around the
edge of these pages are examples
of each of the seven
crystal systems.

*This yellow baryte
crystal is orthorhombic.
Baryte is also found in
several other colours.*

### Crystal glass
We often see glasses and vases
labelled "crystal". This actually
means that they are made from a
particularly clear type of glass called
crystal glass, although glass is not
crystalline at all. Instead of having
a regularly repeating pattern of
atoms like a real crystal, glass is
amorphous, which means that its
atoms are much more randomly
arranged than those in crystals.

*Pyrite crystals are cubic and are
sometimes known as "fool's gold",
as they can be mistaken for gold.*

## DEMONSTRATING CRYSTALLIZATION

**A CRYSTAL CAN** be grown from a solution of copper sulphate. This demonstration must be done by an adult in a science lab, as copper sulphate is poisonous. It is important to wash hands after handling copper sulphate. **The demonstrator will need**: water; copper sulphate; shallow dish; cotton thread; piece of card; glass jar.

The crystal after three weeks

*Three days*

*Five days*

**1** Copper sulphate is dissolved in water to make a strong solution. A small amount of this solution is poured into a shallow dish and left to evaporate.

**2** As the water evaporates, the solution reaches the point of saturation. The solution can no longer hold the copper sulphate, so small crystals start to grow.

**3** In a few days, crystals cover the dish. The largest crystal is removed. Cotton is tied around it and it is suspended from the card in a jar of the remaining copper sulphate solution. This crystal is a "seed" for further crystallization, and will continue to grow. You can grow salt crystals using this same method with a salt solution.

*Although attractive, axinite crystals are too brittle to be used as gemstones. Their structure is triclinic in shape.*

## LIQUID CRYSTALS

Most calculators have a liquid crystal display (LCD). Liquid crystal pours like a liquid but has a structure similar to a crystal. It is sandwiched between two thin pieces of glass in an LCD. When light passes through an LCD, it reflects off the mirror behind it and makes the display look light. The top piece of glass has a conductive coating. Any electricity flowing through it changes the arrangement of the liquid crystal molecules directly beneath, and stops light reflecting back, making that section of the display look dark.

*Liquid crystal seen through a microscope*

*A calculator with an LCD display*

*These gypsum crystals are an example of the monoclinic crystal system. They are "twinned", which means they are joined along one edge.*

*Purple-coloured quartz is known as amethyst. This trigonal crystal is used as a gemstone.*

*Zircon is a gemstone with a tetragonal structure. It is found in various different colours.*

*The gemstone aquamarine is a blue-green beryl crystal with a hexagonal structure.*

# LIQUIDS

**IF YOU POUR MILK INTO A CUP,**
it takes the shape of the cup. Pour it into a
wine glass and it takes the shape of the glass.
All liquids are fluids – they flow, or pour, and
take the shape of any container they are put
in. Like all matter, liquids are made of particles,
or molecules. In solids, these particles attract one
another strongly and form a rigid structure. In
liquids, the particles are less strongly attracted and
can move about, usually in bundles. If conditions
change, liquids can change state. They can freeze and
become solids, or they can evaporate and become gases.

*Liquid chocolate is poured into a
mould. The chocolate will freeze
solid in the shape of the mould.*

## DEMONSTRATING BOILING POINTS

**HOW DO LIQUIDS EVAPORATE?** When some of the molecules near the
surface move fast enough, they escape into the air. As the temperature
rises, more surface molecules escape. At a certain temperature, all of the
molecules move fast enough to escape, and the liquid boils. Boiling liquids
are very hot, so this experiment must be done by an adult in a science lab.

**The demonstrator will
need**: heat-proof container;
heat source (such as a
Bunsen burner); selection
of liquids; thermometer
that goes up to 360°C
(680°F); heat-proof
gloves; tongs.

**1** A small amount of liquid
is heated in the heat-proof
container. Using gloves and
tongs, the thermometer is
dipped into the liquid. The
temperature starts to rise.

**2** Soon the liquid will
bubble. The temperature
stops rising and remains
constant. The liquid has now
reached its boiling point. This
temperature is recorded. The
procedure is repeated with
other liquids and the results
compared. It is clear that the
boiling point is different for
different liquids.

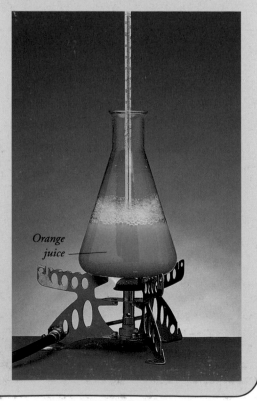

*Orange juice*

## FREEZING SOLID

In a liquid, the molecules are free to move around.
But the lower the temperature, the slower they
move and the more they attract one another. At
a certain temperature, the molecules attract one
another so strongly that they move very little,
and the liquid turns into a solid. We say the
liquid freezes. Every liquid becomes solid at
a different temperature – its freezing point.

**Evaporation and condensation**
When water evaporates into the air, it forms water vapour
(a gas). As the vapour rises into cooler air, the molecules
in the vapour slow down. Eventually, they start strongly
attracting one another, and the vapour turns into droplets
of liquid water. This process, called condensation,
creates clouds and then rain.

**TEST THE VISCOSITY OF** different liquids by dropping marbles into them. The longer a marble takes to fall, the higher the liquid's viscosity. **You will need**: identical glasses or jars; selection of liquids (see examples below); marbles of the same size and weight.

**1** Pour the liquids into identical glasses or jars, filling them to the same level. Drop marbles into two of them at the same time and from the same height. The first marble to hit the bottom is in the least viscous liquid.

**2** Compare the viscosity of all the liquids by noting which marble hits the bottom first each time. Make a list of the liquids in order of their viscosity. You could also try gently warming the liquids to see how this affects viscosity.

*Syrup*

*Vegetable oil*

*Red wine vinegar*

*Bubble bath*

# VISCOSITY

When you pour water into a glass, it flows easily and fills the glass quickly. If you try the same thing with syrup, it flows much more slowly. Syrup is a thicker liquid than water and has a higher viscosity. Viscosity is a measure of a liquid's resistance to flow. It is a kind of internal friction. Viscosity in liquids is put to good use to make lubricants, such as engine oil. The oil helps separate the moving metal parts of engines to stop them rubbing together. Gases have viscosity too, though much less than liquids.

*Syrup forms coils as it pours due to its high viscosity.*

## ‹ TAKING SHAPE ›

Liquids take the shape of their container. But what shape do they take when they are on their own? A good place to find out is on a spacecraft in microgravity (almost zero gravity), where water forms a sphere. A force between its molecules called surface tension makes it form this shape. But a water drop on a leaf forms a teardrop shape because gravity tugs at it. 26, 70 ▶

*Gravity distorts the shape of the water drop.*

# WATER

**THE MOST COMMON SUBSTANCE ON THE FACE OF THE**
Earth is water, which covers nearly three-quarters of our planet. Water is vital to the survival of life on Earth. It is unlike most other substances because it exists in all three states of matter – solid, liquid, and gas. Water is usually found as a liquid, for example, in our vast oceans. However, water also exists as a solid in the form of ice and snow, and as a gas in the form of water vapour in the air. Another unusual property of water is its ability to dissolve many other substances. Water is one of the best solvents we know. The substances that do not dissolve in water can often be filtered out to make cleaner water.

## THE WATER CYCLE

Water constantly circulates between the Earth's surface and the atmosphere. This is called the water cycle. As the Sun heats the water molecules on the surface, these molecules evaporate, turning to vapour. The water vapour rises and cools, condensing into droplets that form clouds. When the drops get big enough, they fall back to the surface as rain, or snow if the air is cold enough.

### Water as a liquid

The Earth's average temperature is ideal for water to exist as a liquid. It is not so hot that the water evaporates quickly, nor is it so cold that the water freezes. As in all liquids, the molecules in water tend to gather together in bundles. These bundles have the ability to slide over one another, allowing liquid water to flow easily.

### Water as a gas

At most temperatures, molecules gradually escape from the surface of liquid water to form a gas, or vapour. This process of evaporation becomes quicker as the temperature rises. At sea level, water boils at 100°C (212°F), causing rapid evaporation. What we call steam forms when the hot vapour cools in the air to make a cloud of water drops.

### Molecules in motion

The chemical formula of water is $H_2O$. This shows that a molecule of water is made up of two hydrogen atoms (H) and one oxygen atom (O). The oxygen atom is much bigger than the two hydrogen atoms. This computer graphic shows the molecules in liquid water. They are much closer together than they are in water vapour and they move more slowly.

### Water as a solid

As liquid water cools, the bundles of molecules move closer together. However, when water cools to 0°C (32°F), a strange thing happens. The molecules move further apart and freeze into the solid structure that is ice. In other words, when water freezes, it expands and becomes lighter. That is why ice floats on water.

**THE WATER FROM** our taps looks crystal clear, but it didn't start out that way. Originally, it came from rivers, lakes, or reservoirs, and it contained bits of dirt and other matter. This experiment shows how to remove dirt from water by filtering. **You will need:** an adult to help you; two beakers; clear plastic drink bottle; knife; dirty water (tap water mixed with a combination of bagged potting compost, rice, flour, tea leaves, coffee grounds); large dish; filter paper (such as that used in coffee makers); charcoal; sand; gravel.

**1** Ask an adult to cut off the top of the bottle, and make a hole in the bottom of it. Line the bottom of the bottle with filter paper.

**2** Stand the bottle in the dish. Fill it with a layer of charcoal at the bottom, then a layer of sand, and finally a layer of gravel at the top. Pour the dirty water into the top of the bottle.

**3** As the water seeps through the bottle, the layers filter out smaller and smaller particles of dirt. The gravel traps the coarsest particles, while the filter paper traps the finest particles. The result is cleaner water. However, there are still invisible chemicals and germs in the water, so do not drink it!

*Dirty water*

*Gravel*

*Charcoal*

*Sand*

*Filter paper*

*Hole in bottle*

*Filtered water in dish*

### Water recycling
These large beds of sand in Florida, USA, help to filter out impurities from the water. The clean water is then used to irrigate groves of orange and lemon trees. Modern cities produce huge amounts of dirty water and sewage every day. This watery waste must be treated before it can be recycled into the environment. First, dirty particles are filtered out of the water, then chemicals such as chlorine are added to kill germs.

*Sand beds recycle water in the same way as the experiment above, but on a much larger scale.*

# LIQUID DENSITY

**DENSITY IS THE AMOUNT OF MASS** in a certain volume. Compare a substance of large, closely-packed molecules with a second substance of small, well-spaced molecules. The first substance will have a greater mass per volume, and will therefore be denser than the second substance. The liquid metal mercury, for example, is much denser than water. In general, solids are denser than liquids, and liquids denser than gases. However, density can change, for instance, by heating or cooling a liquid.

*Different liquids separate according to their densities.*

*Cooking oil*

*Water*

*Syrup*

# LIQUID LAYERS

Liquids with different densities float on top of one another in layers. You can demonstrate this with oil, water, and syrup. First, pour some syrup into a glass. Then pour in some cooking oil. Because the oil is less dense, it floats on top of the syrup. Now pour in some water. The water forms a layer between the other two liquids because it is denser than the oil, but less dense than the syrup.

*An oil slick floating on the sea can cause serious damage to the environment.*

### Oil and water
Oil is made up of tangled strings of molecules that are more spaced out than water molecules. As a result, oil has a lower density and can float on water (as shown above). In our everyday world, this property of oil can have serious consequences. Oil slicks float on the surface of the sea, causing harmful pollution. The oil can kill sea birds and other marine life, and contaminate beaches. Oil fires are another problem. They cannot be extinguished with water because the burning oil floats on top of the water. Oil fires must be tackled with special foam.

### ‹ ROADSIDE RAINBOWS ›
Have you noticed the rainbow colours in puddles at the side of the road? They are caused by drops of oil spilt by passing traffic. The oil floats on the water in the puddles and spreads out as a thin film. When light hits the puddles, it is reflected both from the film of oil and from the water underneath. The two beams interfere with each other and some of the wavelengths, or colours, in the light cancel each other out. The result is a constantly changing pattern of rainbow colours. 118 ▶

*Oily puddles create rainbow effects.*

*The spacious, fixed pattern of molecules in ice means that ice is less dense than liquid water.*

*The coloured hot water rises because it is less dense than the surrounding cold water.*

**MAKE AN UNDERWATER** volcano to see how heat lowers the density of water. **You will need**: a large jar; a small bottle that will fit inside the jar; a long piece of string; cold tap water; hot tap water; food colouring.

**1** Fill the jar three-quarters full with cold water. Loop the string firmly around the neck of the bottle to act as a handle. Fill the bottle with hot tap water and add food colouring to the hot water.

**2** Carefully lower the bottle of hot water into the jar using the string handle. Watch as the hot, coloured water rises out of the bottle, like lava from an erupting volcano. Heat gives the water molecules energy, causing them to move farther apart and take up more space. In other words, the hot water is less dense than the cold water, so it rises to the top of the jar.

**3** After a while, the molecules of hot and cold water will mix, causing the water temperature throughout the jar to even out.

*Cold water molecules are closely packed together. They do not have enough energy to move very far.*

*As water heats up, the molecules gain energy. If enough heat is applied, they will fly off to become water vapour.*

### Unusual ice
When most liquids freeze into solids, the molecules squeeze more closely together and the density increases. Water is different. Its solid form (ice) is less dense than its liquid form. This is why ice floats on water. The molecules in liquid water are packed together but can still move around. The molecules in ice are fixed in a rigid lattice pattern, with space between them. They take up more room than molecules in the liquid form, making ice less dense. This unusual property of water is vital to underwater life. Ice floating on the surface acts as a barrier to stop the water underneath from freezing.

# SALT WATER
When substances dissolve in a liquid, the density of the liquid increases. The dissolving molecules mix with the liquid molecules, so each drop of liquid now has more molecules in it. Sea water has salt and other substances dissolved in it that makes it more dense than fresh water. The Dead Sea, on the borders of Israel and Jordan, is the world's saltiest and densest body of water. Nearly 25 per cent of the water is dissolved salts – more than six times the amount in ordinary sea water. Due to the hot climate, any water that flows into the Dead Sea evaporates quickly, leaving the salt behind. The concentration of salt in the water is so high that the only living things that can make their home there are bacteria.

*People can float effortlessly in the Dead Sea because their bodies are less dense than the salty water.*

# FLOATING AND SINKING

**AN OBJECT THAT IS LESS DENSE THAN WATER, SUCH AS A** log, can float in water. An object that is more dense, such as a rock, will sink. More than 2,000 years ago, a Greek scientist named Archimedes (C 278–212 BC) found that an object weighs less in water than in air because the upwards force of the water, called upthrust or buoyancy, partly supports the object. If an object is less dense than the water beneath it, the upthrust will support its entire weight and the object will float. Notice that an object in water displaces some of that water, pushing it aside. The amount of upthrust exerted on the object equals the weight of this displaced water.

**Eureka!**
Archimedes' principle states that the weight of an object is equal to the weight of the liquid that the object displaces. He is said to have made his discovery when he stepped into his bath and noticed the water in the tub rising. Excited, Archimedes rushed naked into the street, crying "Eureka!", meaning "I've got it!". He used his findings to prove that King Hieron's crown was not pure gold.

## FLOATING STEEL

Huge ships, like the *Queen Elizabeth 2*, are made from steel plates that weigh tens of thousands of tonnes. How do such heavy ships float? The secret is in the structure. The hull of a large ship takes up a great deal of volume, but its overall density is less than the density of water. The weight of the water that it displaces equals the weight of the ship. In other words, the displaced water creates an upwards force (upthrust) that exactly balances the downwards force of the ship's weight.

## LET'S EXPERIMENT
### MAKING THINGS FLOAT

**IF YOU DROP** a glass marble into some water, it sinks to the bottom because glass is denser than water. The weight of the marble causes a downwards force that is greater than the upthrust of the water being displaced. Modelling clay is also denser than water. However, you can make modelling clay float by changing the shape to increase its volume and decrease its density. **You will need:** ball of modelling clay; glass or beaker of water; some marbles.

**1** Drop the clay ball into the glass of water. It sinks to the bottom because modelling clay is denser than water.

**2** Now shape the modelling clay into a boat with a wide bottom and high sides. Place it in the water and watch it float. Its bigger shape displaces a larger volume of water which is heavy enough to balance the weight of the modelling clay. You may find that the clay boat will even hold the marbles.

## BUOYANCY

Our bodies are lighter than water, allowing us to float on the water's surface. However, this natural buoyancy makes it harder to swim underwater, because the water's upthrust tries to push the body up to the surface. This causes a particular problem for deep-sea divers, who spend long periods of time underwater. To resist buoyancy, divers wear belts with heavy lead weights attached. Their total weight acting downwards balances the upthrust. In this state of neutral buoyancy, divers are in effect weightless, rather like an astronaut in orbit.

*Diver's belt containing weights*

### ◄ LOAD LINES ►

Boats ride high in dense water because they have to displace less water in order to float. Salty sea water is denser than fresh water, and cold sea water is densest of all. A boat fully loaded in cold seas may sink if it sails into warm seas or into a river. To prevent this, boats have Plimsoll lines to indicate maximum load level in different waters.

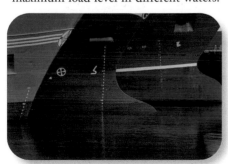

*These fishing boats are unloaded, so they have less density and sit high in the water.* **22 ►**

**MAKE A TOY DIVER** that dives and surfaces according to Archimedes' principle. **You will need:** modelling clay; plastic pen cap; glass; water; paper clips; plastic drinks bottle with lid.

**1** Fix a lump of modelling clay to the end of the plastic pen cap. Adjust the amount of clay until the top of the cap just floats above the surface in a glass of water. A bubble of air trapped inside the cap makes it light enough to float.

*Seal any holes in the tip of the pen cap with modelling clay.*

**2** Use paper clips to make a hook and weights. Now put your diver into a full bottle of water and screw on the lid.

**3** Gently squeeze the bottle. The diver sinks as extra water pushes into the pen cap, forcing the air bubble to shrink. The diver is now too heavy to float.

**4** Release the bottle. The diver rises as the extra water leaves the cap, making it light enough to float again. Experiment with the number of paper clips to see how the extra weight affects your diver.

*To float, ballast tanks are full of air.*

*To dive, water floods into the ballast tanks, making the submarine heavier.*

*To rise, air is pumped into the ballast tanks, making the submarine lighter.*

## SUBMARINES

A submarine works in a similar way to the toy diver above. Special chambers called ballast tanks are filled with either air or water. On the surface, the tanks are full of air. The submarine's weight balances the upthrust of the water, so it floats. To dive, water is let into the tanks, making the submarine heavier. The submarine's weight is now greater than the upthrust, so it sinks. To surface, compressed air is blown into the tanks to force out the water and make the submarine lighter again.

# SURFACE TENSION

**CAREFULLY PLACE A STEEL PAPER CLIP IN A GLASS** of water so that it floats on the surface. Steel is denser (heavier) than water, so how does the paper clip float? Water and many other liquids behave as if they have a skin on the surface. It is this "skin" that supports the paper clip. The "skin" on liquids is caused by the inwards pull on molecules at the surface. The effect is called surface tension, and it explains how insects can walk on water, why the dew on a spider's web forms tiny, round drops, and why water alone cannot "wet" greasy plates.

## ROUND DROPS

Surface tension causes drops of water to form spherical shapes. In the middle of a drop, the molecules are attracted equally in all directions by the molecules around them. At the surface, there are no molecules above to pull outwards, leaving only an inwards attraction. This inwards force pulls the surface into a shape with as small a surface area as possible – a sphere.

## WALKING ON WATER

A pond skater skims quickly over the stretchy skin formed by surface tension on the water. The pond skater distributes its weight over a large area by spreading out its legs. The skin stretches slightly under the weight of the tiny insect, but is strong enough to support it.

**Leakproof fabric**
Fix a gauze bandage over the end of a bottle of water. Turn the bottle upside-down – the water will not pour out. It is held inside by the surface tension of the water in the holes between the gauze threads. Fabric tents stop rain from getting through in a similar way.

*Secure the gauze bandage over the end of the open bottle with an elastic band.*

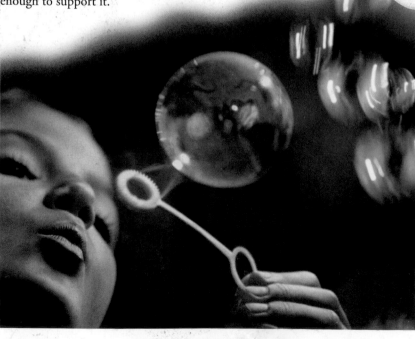

## BUBBLE POWER

Dip a circle of wire or plastic into a mixture of washing-up liquid, glycerine, and water. Surface tension causes a skin of soapy water to form across the circle. Blow against the skin, and it stretches to form spherical bubbles. The glycerine makes the solu___ ___icker so the bubbles don't burst as easily.

### Adhesion and cohesion

A contained liquid often has a curved surface, which is called the meniscus. Water in a glass tube (left) has a meniscus that curves up at the edges because water molecules are more attracted to glass molecules than to one another. We call this force adhesion. Mercury in a glass tube (right) has a meniscus that curves down at the edges. Its molecules attract one another more than they attract the glass molecules. This force is called cohesion.

### Capillary action

Place a narrow tube in certain liquids and the liquid rises inside the tube. This is called capillary action. It occurs when the liquid molecules are more attracted to the molecules of the tube than they are to one another. Towels dry by means of capillary action in their fibres.

## LET'S EXPERIMENT
## SURFACE TENSION

**CERTAIN SUBSTANCES CAN** break down surface tension in a liquid. In this experiment, the surface tension of the milk initially holds the drops of food colouring in place. However, what will happen to the drops of food colouring when you add washing-up liquid to the dish? **You will need:** shallow dish; milk; two eye-droppers; food colouring; washing-up liquid.

**2** Using a different dropper, squeeze some washing-up liquid onto the milk. Watch the colours spread as the flexible skin on the milk starts to break down where the drops of washing-up liquid fall. The stronger surface tension around the edge of the dish then pulls the milk and food colouring outwards.

**1** Pour milk into a shallow dish and leave it to warm up to room temperature. Using an eye-dropper, carefully squeeze a few drops of different food colourings onto the surface. Notice that the drops of food colouring form separate circles on the surface. The food colouring does not break the surface tension of the milk.

*The food colouring and the milk swirl into one another.*

# GASES

## WE CAN'T USUALLY SEE OR FEEL THEM, BUT GASES

are just as real as the other two states of matter – solids and liquids. It's just that the molecules in gases are much further apart. We live at the bottom of a vast layer of gas – the air in our atmosphere. Air is not just one gas but a mixture of several, the main ones being nitrogen and oxygen – the gas we must breathe to stay alive. Air is typically colourless and odourless. But other gases are coloured, such as the yellowish-green chlorine. Some smell, such as hydrogen sulphide, which stinks of rotten eggs!

## GAS ON THE MOVE

The molecules in gases are in constant motion, and travel very fast indeed. For example, at room temperature, air molecules travel at speeds of about 1,600 km (1,000 miles) an hour. Because they move so fast, gases quickly fill any container they are put in. And because their molecules are far apart, gases have a much lower density than solids and liquids. A litre of a typical gas at room temperature and pressure weighs only a little more than a gram. A litre of water under the same conditions weighs a kilogram.

*Gas molecules travel swiftly and in all directions.*

## THE GAS LAWS

The properties of gases are different from those of solids and liquids. Solids have a definite volume and shape. Liquids have a definite volume and no definite shape. But gases have no definite volume or shape. They take the volume of their container, and can be squeezed into a smaller volume by pressure. Increasing the temperature of gases can increase their volume or their pressure. Thus, the volume, pressure, and temperature of gases are all related, and are described by three gas laws.

**Boyle's law**
English chemist Robert Boyle first stated this law in 1662. It says that if the temperature of a gas is constant, its pressure ($P$) increases as its volume ($V$) decreases. Mathematically, $P \times V$ = constant.

**Pressure law**
This law states that if the volume of a gas is constant, its pressure ($P$) increases as its temperature ($T$) goes up. Mathematically, $P / T$ = constant. This law follows from the other laws.

**Charles' law**
French scientist Jacques Charles first stated this law in about 1787. It says that if the pressure of a gas is constant, its volume ($V$) increases as its temperature ($T$) goes up. Mathematically, $V / T$ = constant.

*Volume*

*Pressure*  *Temperature*

# GAS DIFFUSION

Because gases travel very fast, they mix rapidly and completely with one another. This process is called diffusion. We can smell a flower because its scent molecules diffuse through the air into our noses. Gases can also diffuse into and out of liquids. This happens in our lungs, where oxygen diffuses from the air into the blood, and carbon dioxide diffuses out of the blood and into the air. Gases diffuse into solids, too. This is often done during the production of microchips (p. 145), in a process called doping, in which pure silicon is impregnated with different elements.

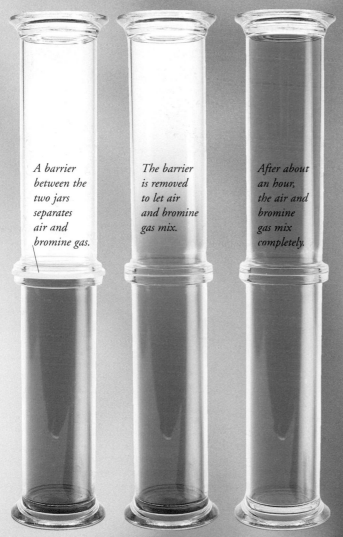

*A barrier between the two jars separates air and bromine gas.*

*The barrier is removed to let air and bromine gas mix.*

*After about an hour, the air and bromine gas mix completely.*

**Bromine gas diffusing in air**

## LET'S EXPERIMENT
### CREATE A GAS

**WHEN YOU FIRST UNSCREW** the cap of a fizzy drinks bottle, gas bubbles rush out of the liquid. This gas is carbon dioxide. In this experiment, we make carbon dioxide using a simple chemical reaction. **You will need**: an adult present; narrow-necked bottle; funnel; small uninflated balloon; vinegar; small amount of bicarbonate of soda (bicarb).

**1** Pour vinegar into the bottle until it is about one-quarter full. Using the funnel, fill the uninflated balloon with bicarb. Carefully stretch the neck of the balloon over the neck of the bottle, making sure no bicarb falls in.

**2** Quickly upend the balloon so that the bicarb falls into the vinegar. The vinegar, which is an acid, attacks the bicarb, releasing carbon dioxide gas. The mixture starts fizzing vigorously, and the balloon begins to inflate with the gas. Turn your face away from the balloon in case it pops.

*Carbon dioxide gas inflates the balloon.*

*Vinegar*

*Vinegar and bicarb mix, producing carbon dioxide gas.*

### Sublimation

Most solid substances, such as metals and fat, melt (turn into a liquid) if they are heated enough. And with more heating, the liquid eventually turns into gas. But some substances are different. For example, when iodine (below) is heated, it turns directly into a purple gas without melting into a liquid first. This process is called sublimation. Dry ice (frozen carbon dioxide) does the same, turning directly into gas as it warms up.

# AIR

## WE CAN'T SEE IT OR TASTE IT, BUT AIR IS ALL

around us. We live at the bottom of a great ocean of air called the atmosphere. Without the atmosphere, there would be no life on Earth. The atmosphere gives us oxygen to breathe, filters out dangerous rays from the Sun, and acts like a blanket to keep Earth at a habitable temperature. By burning fuels, such as petrol in cars, more and more carbon dioxide is released into the atmosphere, making it trap more and more heat. This global warming seems to be affecting weather patterns around the world.

*Aurorae (Northern and Southern Lights)*

*Exosphere above 500 km*

*Space shuttle*

*Meteor trails*

*Thermosphere 80-500 km*

*Mesosphere 50-80 km*

*Weather balloon*

*Stratosphere 20-50 km*

*Aeroplane*

*Troposphere 0-20 km*

## ATMOSPHERE

The atmosphere has five layers. The troposphere is the nearest to the Earth's surface. This is also where most of our weather takes place. The stratosphere contains the ozone layer, which filters out deadly rays from the Sun. Above this, the mesosphere is very cold, with temperatures dropping to -100°C (-148°F). In the thermosphere, temperatures rise again due to the Sun's energy, reaching 1,800°C (3,300°F). The top layer is the exosphere, where the atmosphere gradually merges into space.

**Hot air**
Hot-air balloons rise into the morning sky. Burning gas heats the air inside a balloon. As the air in the balloon gets hotter, it also expands and becomes lighter (less dense) than the cold air outside, causing the balloon to rise.

## GASES IN THE AIR

Air is a mixture of gases, but only nitrogen and oxygen exist in large amounts. Air comprises 78 per cent nitrogen, 21 per cent oxygen, and only one per cent other gases. These balloons show the proportion of different gases in the air. Blue represents nitrogen, red represents oxygen, and white represents all other gases. Humans and other animals breathe in oxygen from the dense air in the troposphere. The one per cent of other gases includes carbon dioxide and water vapour, which are both vital for life on Earth. Plants take in carbon dioxide to make food, while water vapour controls the weather.

**ALL OF THE GASES IN AIR** have different properties. Carbon dioxide, for example, is denser than air and does not support combustion, meaning that things can't burn in carbon dioxide like they can in oxygen. These two properties make carbon dioxide an ideal material for a fire extinguisher. **You will need:** an adult present; small candle; shallow bowl; match; bottle; bicarbonate of soda; vinegar.

**1** Place a small candle into a shallow bowl and carefully light the wick. Pour bicarbonate of soda into a bottle, followed by some vinegar. The mixture fizzes and gives off an invisible gas. This is carbon dioxide. Cover the bottle with your thumb to hold in the carbon dioxide gas.

**2** Carefully, bring the open end of the bottle over the burning candle and remove your thumb. The dense carbon dioxide gas sweeps away the oxygen, putting out the flame.

*Because carbon dioxide gas is denser than air, it falls from the bottle and puts out the flame.*

*Take care not to spill any liquid.*

# FIRST ATMOSPHERE

More than four billion years ago, erupting volcanoes created Earth's original atmosphere. Volcanoes spewed out gases such as nitrogen, carbon dioxide, and water vapour. As Earth cooled, most of the water vapour condensed out of the atmosphere to form oceans. Volcanoes, such as Popocateptl in Mexico (above), still emit dust, carbon dioxide, and water vapour into the atmosphere.

**WHAT HAPPENS WHEN FIRE** is starved of oxygen? How can we estimate the amount of oxygen contained in air? Many scientists have used this experiment to find out more about air. **You will need:** an adult present; candle; adhesive putty; shallow bowl of water; match; jar with wide opening.

**1** Stick a piece of adhesive putty into the middle of the shallow bowl. Now stick the candle on the adhesive putty, making sure that the candle stands securely. Pour water into the bowl so it is about two-thirds full. Light the candle. Carefully place the jar upside-down over the candle to close off the air supply. Take note of the water level in the jar.

**2** Notice the water level in the jar rises as the candle burns. The flame uses up the oxygen inside the jar, causing extra water to fill the available space.

**3** Soon, the flame goes out because it has used up all of the oxygen in the jar. Note the water level again. The water in the jar has risen to take the place of the used-up oxygen.

*The flame burns in oxygen.*

*Note the water level in the jar.*

*The flame goes out when the oxygen is used up.*

*The water level in the jar rises to take the place of the oxygen.*

# FLUID PRESSURE

**DID YOU KNOW THAT YOU ARE CARRYING A**
15-tonne weight? This is the force caused by
the air in the atmosphere pressing on the
outside of your body. You can't feel this
pressure because the air inside your
body is pressing back with the same
force. The large weight of air above our
heads gives air its pressure. All fluids –
gases and liquids – exert pressure in
a similar way. In science, pressure has
a precise meaning. It means the force
pressing down on a certain area, and
is measured in units of newtons per
square metre (pascals).

## RESISTING THE PRESSURE

The pressure at any point in a fluid depends on the
weight of fluid above it. Pressures are much greater in
liquids than in gases because they are denser and weigh
more. In water, the pressure 10 m (33 ft) beneath the
surface is twice atmospheric pressure – the pressure
at the surface. Some 30 m (98 ft) down, the pressure is
four times atmospheric pressure. Divers who descend
deep into the sea experience even greater pressure
that could crush their bodies. To avoid this, they
wear special metal suits built to withstand high
pressures, like this Newtsuit (right).

### The deepest depths
The deepest parts of the oceans can be explored only by
special submarines with pressure-resistant hulls. The Deep
Submergence Vehicle (DSV) *Alvin* (below) can reach depths
of 4,500 m (14,800 ft). The deepest-diving craft are called
bathyscaphes. *Trieste* was one that descended to a record
depth of nearly 11 km (7 miles) in 1960.

# WATER ENERGY

Engineers harness water pressure
to produce electric power. We call
it hydroelectric ("water-electric")
power. It provides about a quarter
of the world's electricity. Most
hydroelectric power plants are built
at the foot of dams, which hold
back reservoirs (stores) of water.
Water is piped from the bottom of
a reservoir through the dam to the
power plant. There it flows through
turbines and spins them round. The
turbines in turn spin generators to
make electricity. Since water is piped
from the bottom of the reservoir, it
is at high pressure.

*The Glen Canyon Dam and
hydroelectric plant on the
Colorado River, Arizona, USA*

**AIR PRESSURE IN THE** atmosphere is always changing as warm air rises (low pressure) and cold air sinks (high pressure). By measuring the pressure in different places, scientists can tell how the weather is changing. They measure air pressure with barometers. You can make a simple one at home. **You will need:** glass or mug; balloon; elastic bands; double-sided tape; straw; wooden board; card; scissors.

**1** Carefully stretch a balloon over the top of an empty glass. Hold it in place with strong elastic bands. Tape the glass to the wooden board. Cut the end of the straw to a point. Stick the uncut end to the balloon. Make a scale with card.

**2** Fix the scale to the board so that the straw pointer reaches the scale. When the air pressure outside rises, the air inside the glass contracts (gets smaller), causing the balloon to dip and the end of the straw to move up.

**3** When the air pressure outside drops, the air inside the glass expands, pushing the balloon up and the straw downwards.

*Air pressing against the bottom of the card stops the water from falling out.*

**4** Mark the level of the straw each day to record the changes in air pressure. The pointer rises as the air pressure outside increases, and falls as air pressure drops. Falling pressure can indicate that bad weather is on its way.

## AIR PRESSURE

The air in the atmosphere presses down on our bodies with a force of about 100 kilopascals or 1 kg on every square centimetre (14.7 pounds on every square inch). This is called atmospheric pressure. The air doesn't just press down – it presses in all directions, including upwards. This can be shown with a little trick. Fill a glass right to the brim with water and put a card on top. Pressing your hand against the card, turn the glass upside-down. Now take your hand away. The card will stay where it is, held up by air pressure alone.

**Compressed air**
When you pump up the tyres of your bike, you are forcing more air into the same space. You are compressing the air, or increasing its pressure. Compressed air is a useful source of power for driving machines, including pneumatic ("worked by air") drills for breaking up roads (above).

**THE FOOT BRAKES** of cars and the arms of diggers use hydraulic, or liquid-pressure, systems to transmit power. In a hydraulic system, one piston forces liquid through a pipe to push against another piston, as in this experiment. Never hold the icing syringes near your face, as they could pop out suddenly under the pressure. **You will need:** 2 icing syringes; plastic tubing; water.

**1** Fill an icing syringe with water and pump it into a plastic tube. Half-fill a second syringe with water and connect it to the other end of the tube.

**2** Press one of the plungers in, and the other one will be forced out. The water carries the pressure from one piston to the other.

*Plunger forced up*

*Plunger pressed down*

# FLUID FLOW

**THE LARGEST JET AIRLINERS WEIGH** hundreds of tonnes, yet they can climb into the air and fly. They can do this because of forces set up by the air flowing around the wings. The science concerning the flow of fluids – liquids and gases – is known as hydrodynamics. It is important in many fields. For example, it governs the design of aircraft, cars, and even bridges and skyscrapers, which are all affected by the air flowing over them. Similarly, the way water flows affects the design of pipelines, ships, and submarines, and explains why fish and other water creatures are shaped the way they are.

*Thrust of engines acts forwards.*

## HOW FLIGHT WORKS

Aerodynamics is the science concerned with the forces acting on bodies moving through the air. It is the science that explains how aeroplanes can fly. The secret of flight lies in a plane's wings, which create the necessary lifting force to support it in the air. The three other main forces that act on a flying plane are its weight, the thrust, which is the propelling force of its engines, and the air resistance, also known as drag. In steady flight, lift equals weight, and thrust equals drag.

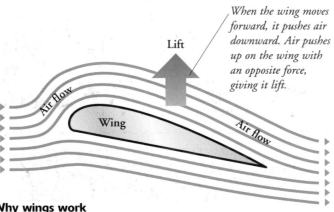

Lift

*When the wing moves forward, it pushes air downward. Air pushes up on the wing with an opposite force, giving it lift.*

Air flow

Wing

Air flow

**Why wings work**
Wings are designed with a special shape called an aerofoil. When air flows past this shape, it is accelerated downwards. The force of this air movement acting downwards is accompanied by an equal and opposite force upwards, which follows from Newton's third law of motion (pp. 64–65). This upwards force is called lift. If the air flows fast enough over the wing, there will be enough lift to support it in the air.

*A dolphin uses its front flippers for steering itself through the water.*

*Smooth, hairless skin helps with streamlining.*

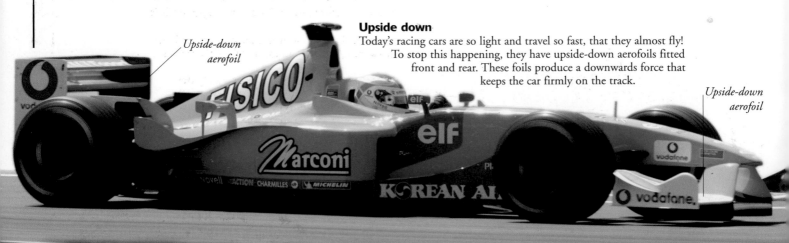

*Upside-down aerofoil*

**Upside down**
Today's racing cars are so light and travel so fast, that they almost fly! To stop this happening, they have upside-down aerofoils fitted front and rear. These foils produce a downwards force that keeps the car firmly on the track.

*Upside-down aerofoil*

*When the wing moves forwards, it pushes air downwards. An opposite force pushes upwards, giving it lift.*

*Drag of air acts backwards.*

*Weight of plane acts downwards.*

# STREAMLINING

When objects travel through fluids, they meet resistance because of friction (pp. 66–67), and this slows them down. Planes experience a lot of air resistance, or drag, and are carefully designed to reduce it to a minimum. First, all the external surfaces are made as smooth as possible. Second, they are streamlined, which means they are shaped so that the air flows smoothly around them. To find the best shape, model planes are tested in wind tunnels, where air is blown past them. Many other objects are now tested in wind tunnels to help streamlining, including ski-wear (right).

**Natural streamlining**
Dolphins are among the ocean's fastest swimmers, perfectly at home in their underwater world. Their bodies are smooth and streamlined so that they slip through the water with the least resistance. They propel themselves with the tail and steer with the front flippers.

**Underwater wings**
Ordinary boats travel relatively slowly because of the resistance of the water on the hull. Hydrofoil boats, such as the one pictured above, can travel much faster because the hull lifts out of the water. The hull is mounted on "underwater wings", or hydrofoils, which develop lift as they travel through the water.

## LET'S EXPERIMENT
### AIR STREAMS

**ANOTHER ASPECT OF FLUID FLOW** is that the pressure in a fluid drops as it moves faster. This is known as the Bernoulli effect, named after the Swiss mathematician Daniel Bernoulli (1700–82). We can use this theory to explain how we are able to make a ping-pong ball hover in the air. **You will need:** a hairdryer set to "cool"; a ping-pong ball.

**1** Hold a hairdryer so that it points upwards. Place the ping-pong ball in the middle of the airstream.

**2** You'll find that the ball will stay put. In the middle, the air flows faster (less pressure) than it does at the edges (higher pressure). The higher pressure always pushes the ball back.

*Switch the hairdryer to a cool setting.*

# MIXTURES AND SOLUTIONS

**WHEN YOU ADD SALT TO SAND AND STIR** them together, you get a mixture. If you taste a bit of this mixture, you'll still find it's salty and gritty. In general, the properties of a mixture are a combination of the properties of the substances mixed together. Mixtures are not the same as compounds. Compounds are substances in which elements are combined chemically with one another. The substances in mixtures aren't combined chemically, and so can usually be easily separated. Solutions are special kinds of mixtures.

*Panning for gold.*

*Heavy gold particles remain in the pan.*

## MANY MIXTURES

Most of the substances we come across in our everyday lives are mixtures. Food is a mixture of substances like carbohydrates, fats, and proteins. Most rocks are solid mixtures of minerals. Oil is a liquid mixture of many hydrocarbons. The air we breathe is a mixture of gases, like nitrogen and oxygen. The substances in mixtures can usually be separated because of differences in their properties. Salt can be separated from sand because it dissolves in water and sand doesn't. Gold can be separated from gravel because it is much heavier. Prospectors (gold-panners) use this property when they pan for gold.

**Some liquids mix** together, others don't. Alcohol and water mix readily together in wines and spirits – they are described as miscible. Oil and water don't mix – they are immiscible. An experiment can show this. **You will need:** cooking oil; water; beaker; food colouring; jug; dropper.

**1** Pour the oil on top of the water in a beaker. They form separate layers because they are immiscible. With an eyedropper, carefully place a drop of food colouring in the oil.

**2** The food colouring stays as a drop because it is also immiscible with oil. Now, push the drop down into the water. It colours the water because it is miscible with water.

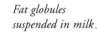

*Fat globules suspended in milk*

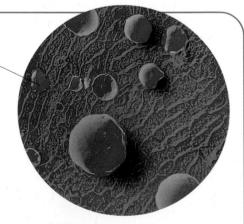

**In suspension**
Smoke and fog are a mixture of particles suspended in air. They are called aerosols. Suspending particles of colouring in a liquid makes most paint suspensions. Milk contains tiny globules (drops) of fat suspended in a liquid. Because the particles aren't solids, milk is called an emulsion.

# IN SOLUTION

When river water flows over chalk rocks, some of the chalk mixes with the water and disappears – it dissolves and forms a chalk solution. What happens is that the chalk molecules mix completely with the water molecules. This always happens when one substance (the solute) dissolves in another (the solvent) to form a solution. Chalk comes out of solution in caves to form stalactites (on the roof) and stalagmites (on the floor). The mineral-rich water that drips into the caves evaporates. The chalk is deposited and builds up to form the icicle-like shapes.

**Dissolved oxygen**
Underwater life in rivers and the seas is made possible because oxygen from the air dissolves in the water. Fish and other water creatures extract the oxygen by means of their gills. This curious creature, called an axolotl, is unusual because its gills (red) are outside the body.

## LET'S EXPERIMENT
### DISTILLING WATER

**IF YOU WERE SHIPWRECKED** on a desert island with no fresh water to drink, how would you survive? You couldn't drink sea water because it's too salty. What you would have to do is remove the salt from the water (distil). This experiment shows how water can be distilled. **You will need:** an adult present; water; salt; a small saucepan; a large pan lid; a dish; a heat source. Make sure you let all equipment cool down before putting it away.

**1** Make up a salt solution by dissolving one tablespoon of salt into two cupfuls of water. Pour into a saucepan and cover with a large lid. Tilt the lid as shown in the picture, and place a dish under the lower end. Ask an adult to help you heat the saucepan on the stove.

**2** As the salt water heats up, it evaporates, or turns to vapour. When the water vapour meets the cool lid, it condenses, or turns back to liquid water, which drips into the dish. Taste this water – it shouldn't be salty. The salt stays behind in the pan.

# ATOMS AND ELEMENTS

**Picture:** *Double-stranded DNA, pictured in false colour by a scanning tunnelling microscope.*

# LITTLE BITS OF MATTER

**EVERY SUBSTANCE WE FIND IN THE WORLD AROUND US, SUCH** as wood, rock, water, or air, is made up of stuff we call matter. There are millions of different kinds of matter, but they are formed from only about 90 basic substances. We call these substances the chemical elements. Gold is an element, for example, because you cannot break it down into simpler substances. In turn, the chemical elements are made up of tiny particles called atoms. All the atoms in each element are identical, and different elements have different kinds of atoms. These ideas form the basis of the atomic theory of matter.

*Scanning tunnelling microscopes (STMs) can "see" atoms and the structures they form. This STM image shows the layered structure of a fatty acid. Fatty acids are essential ingredients of fats.*

## ATOMS AND MOLECULES

In most substances, the atoms are not found on their own. They are found linked to other atoms to form particles we call molecules. In certain elements, the molecules consist of combinations of the same atoms. In other substances, the molecules are combinations of different

*Electrically charged particles produced in nuclear experiments are detected in a bubble chamber. The particles leave a trail of hydrogen bubbles behind as they travel through the chamber.*

atoms. For example, water molecules consist of atoms of the elements hydrogen and oxygen linked together. It is the properties of the molecules that determine what a substance is like. The science that deals with the properties of all the different elements and other substances is called chemistry. Chemists investigate the changes that take place when substances react together. Using chemical reactions, scientists are able to change substances and make new materials.

## SMASHING ATOMS

Scientists once thought that atoms were the smallest particles of matter, but they were wrong. Atoms are made up of even tinier particles, known as subatomic (smaller than the atom) particles. Most of them carry an electric charge. The electron was the first subatomic particle to be discovered, followed by the proton and the neutron. These three are by far the most important. Protons and neutrons are found together in the solid centre (nucleus) of the atom. Much tinier electrons surround the nucleus. More than 200 other subatomic particles have been discovered in experiments in which scientists use beams of accelerated (speeded up) particles

to bombard atoms. The machines they use to do this are called particle accelerators, popularly known as atom-smashers.

## RADIOACTIVE

The atoms of some elements do not need to be smashed before they split up. They are unstable and break down naturally. As they do, they give off streams of radiation. We call these elements radioactive. Fortunately there are not many elements in the world that are radioactive. This is a good thing because the radiation they give out can be harmful. It can damage and kill the body cells and alter the genes, affecting future generations. Of the three kinds of radiation – alpha, beta, and gamma – gamma is the highest energy. Gamma radiation can penetrate most materials.

## NUCLEAR FISSION

The best-known radioactive element is uranium. Its atoms not only break down naturally – they can be made to split apart artificially. Since it is the nucleus of the

Timeline

400 BC Greek philosopher Democritus suggests that all matter is made up of tiny invisible particles that he calls atoms.

c. 350 BC Greek philosopher Aristotle believes matter is made up of four "elements" – earth, air, fire, and water.

1661 Irish scientist Robert Boyle states that matter is made up of primary particles", originating the chemical elements.

1772 French chemist Antoine Lavoisier begins systematic experiments that lay the foundations of chemistry.

1808 English chemist John Dalton proposes that the elements are made up of atoms, and that different elements have different atoms.

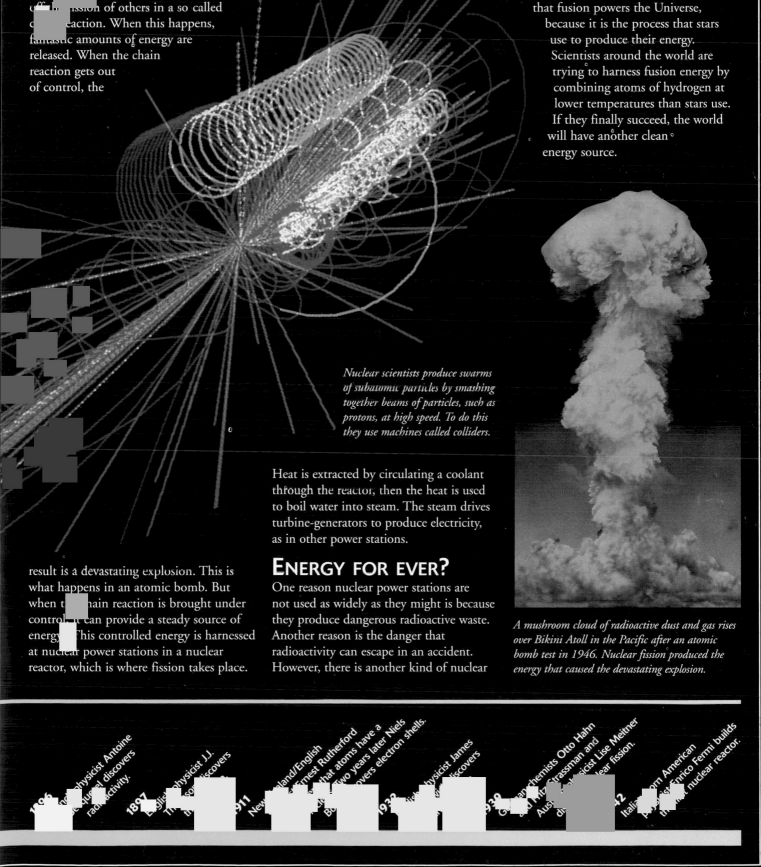

atom that splits, this process is called nuclear fission (splitting). The fission of uranium atom releases a great deal of energy. Under the right conditions, the fission of one atom can trigger off the fission of others in a so called chain reaction. When this happens, fantastic amounts of energy are released. When the chain reaction gets out of control, the

reaction, called fusion, which still produces fantastic amounts of energy, but no radioactivity. In nuclear fusion, atoms are made to fuse (join) together, the opposite of fission. It could be said that fusion powers the Universe, because it is the process that stars use to produce their energy. Scientists around the world are trying to harness fusion energy by combining atoms of hydrogen at lower temperatures than stars use. If they finally succeed, the world will have another clean energy source.

*Nuclear scientists produce swarms of subatomic particles by smashing together beams of particles, such as protons, at high speed. To do this they use machines called colliders.*

Heat is extracted by circulating a coolant through the reactor, then the heat is used to boil water into steam. The steam drives turbine-generators to produce electricity, as in other power stations.

## ENERGY FOR EVER?

result is a devastating explosion. This is what happens in an atomic bomb. But when the chain reaction is brought under control, it can provide a steady source of energy. This controlled energy is harnessed at nuclear power stations in a nuclear reactor, which is where fission takes place.

One reason nuclear power stations are not used as widely as they might is because they produce dangerous radioactive waste. Another reason is the danger that radioactivity can escape in an accident. However, there is another kind of nuclear

*A mushroom cloud of radioactive dust and gas rises over Bikini Atoll in the Pacific after an atomic bomb test in 1946. Nuclear fission produced the energy that caused the devastating explosion.*

1896 French physicist Antoine Becquerel discovers radioactivity.

1897 English physicist J.J. Thomson discovers the electron.

1911 New Zealand/English physicist Ernest Rutherford discovers that atoms have a nucleus. Two years later Niels Bohr discovers electron shells.

1932 English physicist James Chadwick discovers the neutron.

1939 German chemists Otto Hahn and Fritz Strassman and Austrian physicist Lise Meitner discover nuclear fission.

1942 Italian-born American physicist Enrico Fermi builds the first nuclear reactor.

# INSIDE THE ATOM

**ATOMS ARE THE TINY PARTICLES THAT MAKE** up all matter. But just how small are they? They are smaller than you could ever imagine – it would take millions of them side by side to measure 1 cm (0.4 in). Every atom has a central core called a nucleus, with tiny electrons circling around it at high speed. The nucleus takes up only a tiny space, for it is only about one ten-thousandth the size of the atom. If the nucleus were the size of a golf ball, the diameter of an atom would be bigger than the height of the Empire State Building in New York, USA. Most of an atom is actually empty space!

## STRUCTURE OF AN ATOM

Most of an atom's mass rests in the nucleus at the centre. The nucleus contains the two heaviest nuclear particles – protons and neutrons. Much lighter electrons circle around the nucleus, with different groups circling in different layers, or shells. There are as many electrons in an atom as there are protons. The carbon atom, for example, has six protons in the nucleus and six electrons circling round it. Two electrons circle in an inner shell, four electrons in an outer shell.

## LET'S EXPERIMENT
### THE SIZE OF AN ATOM

**IT IS VERY HARD TO** imagine how tiny an atom is. You can gain an idea of its smallness by cutting up a strip of paper. **You will need:** a strip of paper 28 cm (11 in) long; scissors.

**1** Cut the strip in half (cut 1). Discard one half. Now cut the other half in two (cut 2). Continue cutting the strip into halves, discarding one half, as many times as you can. Always cut parallel to the previous cut.

**2** How many cuts did you make before the paper became too small to cut in half again? Probably only about eight. If you wanted to cut the paper until it was as small as an atom, you would have to cut it 30 times!

*The path an electron moves along can be called its "orbit".*

*Electron*

*Inner shell*

Nucleus

Six neutrons (red)

Six protons (grey)

*Outer shell*

**A carbon atom sliced in half**

A neutron
sliced in half

A neutron is made
up of three quarks.

*The three quarks
are held together
by particles
called gluons.*

## THE MAIN PARTICLES

Protons, neutrons, and electrons are the main
particles found in atoms. Protons and
neutrons are much bigger – they are more
than 1,800 times heavier than electrons.
Protons have a tiny positive electric
charge. Neutrons have no charge – they
are neutral. Electrons have a tiny negative
electric charge. The atom is held together
by the attraction between the positive
and negative charges. Because they have
equal numbers of protons and electrons,
atoms are electrically neutral. Electrons are
true basic, or fundamental atomic particles.
But protons and neutrons are not. They are
each made up of three particles called quarks,
which are true fundamental particles.

*The tunnels housing the large accelerators
are marked on the photograph.*

### Particle physics
Physicists divide the 200 or
so known subatomic particles
into a number of families,
which includes quarks, baryons,
mesons, and leptons. Protons
and neutrons are baryons.
Electrons are leptons. Mesons
are found in cosmic rays.
Machines called accelerators
are used to produce and study
these particles. The largest is
found in a circular tunnel near
Geneva, Switzerland. It is
27 km (17 miles) in diameter.

### Ernest Rutherford
(1871–1937)
Born in New Zealand,
Ernest Rutherford
made fundamental
discoveries in nuclear
science. In 1902, he
explained the nature
of radioactivity in his
"theory of atomic transmutation", which
won him the Nobel prize for chemistry
in 1908. Three years later, he proposed his
revolutionary atomic theory that saw the
atom as a kind of solar system, with a
heavy nucleus at the centre and electrons
circling around it. In 1919, Rutherford
carried out the first artificial atomic
transmutation – changing one element
(nitrogen) into another (oxygen). In
this and subsequent transmutations,
Rutherford found that positively charged
hydrogen atoms were always given off,
So he concluded that they must be
common to the nuclei of all atoms.
Rutherford called these particles protons.

## ISOTOPES

All the atoms in an element
contain the same number
of protons, but the
number of neutrons may
vary. Iron, for example, is
made up of four kinds of
atoms, or isotopes, each
with different numbers
of neutrons. Altogether in
nature there are about 320
different isotopes. Most of
them are stable and never
change. But some are unstable.
We call them radioisotopes because they
are radioactive and break down into other elements. Living
things contain traces of a carbon radioisotope, carbon-14
(most of our carbon is carbon-12). Archaeologists can date
ancient remains by the amount of carbon-14 left in them.

*Samples being taken
from an ancient
bone prior to
radiocarbon dating*

### Deadly waste
Radioactive isotopes
give off three kinds
of dangerous radiation.
Alpha rays penetrate
the least and are easily
blocked. Beta rays are
more penetrating, and
gamma rays more
penetrating still. The
fuel elements from
nuclear reactors are
highly radioactive and
are stored in deep pools
of water. The radiation
makes the water
particles glow blue.

# ELEMENTS AND COMPOUNDS

**THE CHEMICAL ELEMENTS ARE THE BUILDING BLOCKS** from which all matter is put together. About 90 elements are found in nature, but we come across only a few on their own. One is graphite, a form of carbon found in pencil leads. Another is gold, found in its pure state in 24-carat jewellery. Most elements are found combined with other elements as compounds – water is a compound of hydrogen and oxygen, for example. In a compound, the elements are not just mixed together. They are linked to one another by strong bonds and cannot simply be separated like mixtures.

**Dalton's atomic theory**

John Dalton
(1766–1844)

Around 400 BC, a Greek philosopher named Democritus suggested that matter was made up of tiny particles he called atoms. However, his idea didn't catch on. It was not until 1808 that this theory on matter was revived. In that year, the English chemist John Dalton put forward his atomic theory, based on years of experimental work. He said that all elements are made up of atoms that cannot be destroyed or split. All the atoms in the same element are similar, and elements are different because they have different atoms.

## BIRTH OF THE ELEMENTS

All the elements in our world came from the stars. Deep inside their cores, stars build up elements in nuclear fusion reactions. They use as their starting point hydrogen, the simplest and most common element in the Universe. First they make it into helium, then transform helium into carbon, and so on. Over time, many elements are produced. When the star dies, it may explode and scatter the elements throughout space, and make new elements in the explosion.

*A star explodes as a supernova in 1987.*

*Galileo space probe carries batteries with plutonium*

**Same but different**

Ordinary oxygen gas is made up of molecules containing two oxygen atoms. But high in the atmosphere there is a layer of oxygen that contains three atoms in each molecule. We call this form of oxygen ozone. Ozone is an allotrope (another form) of oxygen. It is the same element, but put together differently.

**A false-colour image of the Earth's thinning ozone layer**

## ARTIFICIAL ELEMENTS

Of the elements found in nature, uranium has the biggest atom, which contains 92 protons. In 1940, a team of US scientists led by Glenn Seaborg bombarded uranium with deuterons (the nuclei of a heavy isotope of hydrogen) and created a new element containing 94 protons. Called plutonium, it was the first artificial element made. Since then many have been produced, with more than 109 protons in the nucleus. They are known as transuranium elements and, like uranium, they are all radioactive.

# BONDING

Most elements combine with other elements to form compounds. To form a compound, the atoms of one element form links, or bonds, with the atoms of others. Atoms form bonds in different ways, using the electrons in their outer shells. These electrons may be transferred or shared.

## Ionic bonds

When sodium combines with chlorine to form sodium chloride, an electron from the sodium atom is transferred to the chlorine atom. The atoms become electrically charged ions, and the link between them is called an ionic bond.

*Hydrogen atom*

*The two atoms share electrons.*

## Covalent bonds

The atoms of many elements do not readily lose or gain electrons. So they share electrons to form covalent bonds. They share pairs of electrons, each providing one electron to each pair. In the compound ammonia, the nitrogen atom shares its electrons with three hydrogen atoms and takes a share of theirs.

*Nitrogen has five electrons in its outer shell and bonds with three hydrogen atoms to make a stable bond.*

*An electron travels from the sodium atom to the chlorine atom.*

*The sodium atom loses an electron and becomes a positive ion.*

*The chlorine atom gains an electron and becomes a negatively charged ion.*

*Sodium atom*  *Chlorine atom*  ⊕ *Sodium ion*  ⊖ *Chlorine ion*

# MOLECULAR STRUCTURES

The smallest unit of a covalent compound that can exist on its own is the molecule. Ionic compounds do not form individual molecules. They are just collections of positive and negative ions. Chemists may make models of molecules, using balls for atoms and sticks for bonds. They use a chemical formula to describe the make-up of a molecule or compound, using symbols to represent the atoms.

### Many forms
Carbon is found in nature in two very different forms, as graphite and diamond. Graphite is very soft, while diamond is the hardest substance there is. They are different because they have very different structures. We call substances that have different forms polymorphic, meaning "many shapes".

*Hydrogen*

*Carbon*

*Oxygen*

### Carbon dioxide ($CO_2$)
In the molecule, the carbon atom shares pairs of electrons with each oxygen atom.

*Graphite carbon atoms form flat sheets.*

### Ethane ($C_2H_6$)
In the molecule, each carbon atom shares a pair electrons with three hydrogen atoms and also shares a pair of electrons with the other carbon atom.

### Chlorine ($Cl_2$)
The molecule is made up of two chlorine atoms, sharing one pair of electrons.

### Potassium chloride (KCl)
An ionic compound, made up of potassium and chlorine ions held in a lattice.

*Diamond carbon atoms form a 3-D structure.*

# METALS AND NON-METALS

**AMONG THE 90 OR SO ELEMENTS THAT OCCUR** naturally in the world, nearly 70 are metals. They have quite different properties from the remaining elements, which are called non-metals and semimetals. Non-metals include solid elements such as carbon and gaseous elements such as nitrogen. Most metals are shiny, strong, and have a high density and high melting point. They conduct heat and electricity well. In contrast, most non-metals are dull, weak, and have a low density and low melting point. They don't conduct heat and electricity well. The semimetals (metalloids) have properties between metals and non-metals.

## GOOD CONDUCTORS

Metals have a number of properties that distinguish them from other elements. Most metals, for example, are hard and shiny. Gold is used to coat astronauts' visors (above) as it reflects bright sunlight well and doesn't corrode. Most metals are able to conduct, or pass on, heat and electricity. That is why we make pots and pans out of metal and use metal wires to carry electricity. In the atoms of a metal, the electrons are easily shared and drift readily from atom to atom. They can flow throughout the metal carrying heat or electricity.

**Liquid metal**
Mercury is unusual among metals because it is a liquid at room temperature. But it has all the other properties of a typical metal. It is silvery in colour and conducts heat and electricity well.

## SOFT SULPHUR

Sulphur is a typical non-metal. Yellow in colour, it is a soft, light substance that melts easily and doesn't conduct heat or electricity. Sulphur behaves chemically much like oxygen – it is very reactive when it combines with other substances – and is found in the same group in the Periodic Table. On Earth, it is found in its natural state around the vents (openings) from volcanoes. It is also found on volcanoes on Jupiter's moon Io. Sulphur constantly flowing from Io's volcanoes has given the moon its vivid yellow-orange colour.

**A semi-conductor wafer**

**Elements in between**
Some elements are neither true metals nor true non-metals, but have properties in between. They are often called semimetals or metalloids. In their pure state, the semimetals can hardly conduct electricity at all. But when certain elements are added to them, they start to conduct electricity a little. They become semiconductors. Silicon is the most common semiconductor, used to make microchips for computers and other electronic devices (pp. 144–145).

## TOO REACTIVE

Magnesium metal burns rapidly in air with a dazzling white flame (right). It is a highly reactive element. This is the reason we don't find magnesium by itself in nature. We find it combined with other elements in compounds, such as magnesium sulphate (commonly known as Epsom salts). Most other elements are similarly too reactive to be found by themselves. Some exceptions are carbon, sulphur, some gases (such as oxygen), and the precious metals (such as gold). We call elements that can be found in nature native elements.

### Dmitri Mendeleyev (1834–1907)

In the 1800s, chemists began trying to find ways of arranging the elements into some kind of order. Most successful was the Russian chemist Dmitri Mendeleyev. In 1869, he listed the 63 known elements in order of their atomic weights and arranged them into a table. (We now call atomic weight relative atomic mass. It's a way of comparing the masses of the atoms of the elements). He arranged the elements so that they showed a periodic change in properties. Since Mendeleyev created the table, every new element discovered has fitted into the table.

### The noble gases

The elements in the last group in the Periodic Table are gases. They are unusual because they don't combine readily with other elements. Only a few of their compounds have been prepared. Helium, used to fill airships, is one of the most useful of these so-called noble gases.

# THE PERIODIC TABLE

The Periodic Table arranges the elements in a way that brings out their chemical relationships. It is organized into horizontal rows called periods and vertical columns called groups. The groups gather together elements with similar properties. Group I, for example, brings together highly reactive metals like sodium and potassium. Along a period, there is a gradual change in properties. In Period 3, for example, magnesium is less reactive than sodium, and aluminium less reactive than magnesium.

*The atomic number shows the number of protons in the nucleus.*

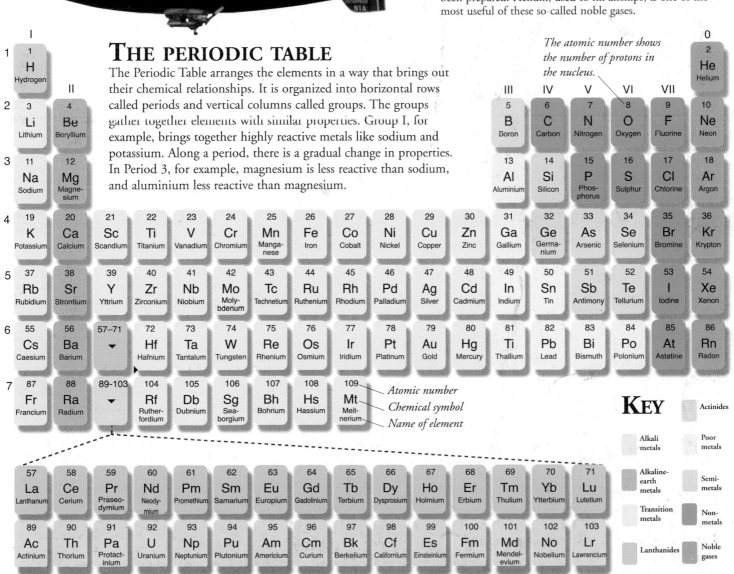

Atomic number
Chemical symbol
Name of element

### KEY

- Actinides
- Alkali metals
- Poor metals
- Alkaline-earth metals
- Semi-metals
- Transition metals
- Non-metals
- Lanthanides
- Noble gases

# CHEMICAL REACTIONS

AROUND US, EVEN INSIDE US, ALL KINDS OF chemicals are constantly coming together and changing into different substances. We call these processes chemical reactions. Chemical reactions take place, for example, when wood burns on a fire, when nails turn rusty, and when you boil an egg. Inside our bodies, they help to keep us alive. Breathing and eating involve the chemical reaction of oxidation, in which oxygen combines with food to produce the energy we need. Oxidation is one of the commonest chemical reactions. Burning and rusting involve oxidation too. Some reactions, such as rusting, take place slowly, whereas others, such as explosions, take place very quickly indeed.

### Oxidation and reduction

In an oxidation reaction, a substance can gain oxygen. It follows, therefore, that another substance has lost oxygen. That loss of oxygen is called reduction. Reactions in which oxidation and reduction go hand in hand are called redox reactions. Iron smelting is a redox reaction. In smelting, carbon is oxidized to carbon dioxide, and iron oxide ore is reduced to iron.

*Iron is obtained from iron ore by a process known as smelting.*

## FAST FIRE

Combustion, or burning, is a fast oxidation reaction. When substances burn, they combine with oxygen in the air and give out energy as heat and light (flames). Fuels such as coal and oil are substances that burn well and give out plenty of energy. They contain a lot of carbon, which combines with the oxygen in the air to form carbon dioxide gas. Reactions that give out energy, like combustion, are termed exothermic. Some reactions, however, take in heat and are known as endothermic. Instant cold packs use endothermic reactions.

## ‹ PHYSICAL CHANGE ›

When iron metal rusts, it changes into another substance, iron oxide. It undergoes a chemical change, and you can't easily get the metal back. When an ice lolly melts, it changes into a liquid. It only undergoes a physical change. It's still the same chemical substance (water) but in a different physical form. 14 ▶

*Ice lollies change their physical state when they melt.*

## SLOW BUT SURE

If shiny new steel nails are left outside, they don't remain shiny for long. They become covered with a reddish-brown coating of rust. The iron in the nails gets attacked by oxygen and moisture in the air to form iron oxide. This process, rusting, is an example of a slow oxidation reaction. The rust layer on iron gradually flakes away, exposing more and more iron to attack. In time the whole metal corrodes and the nail is eaten away. Many metals corrode, but some, such as gold, resist corrosion. That is why gold can remain shiny for centuries.

A catalytic converter

*The catalyst is a thin coating of platinum and rhodium metals on a supporting framework.*

*Exhaust gases from the engine contain pollutants, such as carbon monoxide and nitrogen oxides.*

*Reactions in the converter produce relatively harmless carbon dioxide, nitrogen, and water vapour.*

# SPEEDING UP REACTIONS

Cars produce substances in their exhausts that cause pollution, including carbon monoxide, unburned fuel, and nitrogen oxides. To combat this problem, many are fitted with catalytic converters. These are so called because they convert the pollutants into less harmful gases with the help of a catalyst. A catalyst is a substance that helps bring about and speed up a chemical reaction, but doesn't get changed by the reaction. They reduce the energy needed for the reaction to take place. The reacting substances generally attach to the catalyst, react, and then let go.

## LET'S EXPERIMENT
## A FIZZY REACTION

**CARBONATES ARE COMMON** chemical compounds, in which a metal combines with carbon and oxygen. When acids, such as vinegar, attack carbonates, they release carbon dioxide gas. For this experiment, **you will need:** a glass and a dish; bicarbonate of soda (bicarb); washing powder; vinegar; a spoon; red and blue food colouring.

**1** Mix bicarb, washing powder, blue colouring, and a bit of water in the glass and place it in a dish. Squeeze a few drops of red colouring into the vinegar and pour it into the glass.

**2** The mixture may splutter, so turn your face away first. The mixture fizzes vigorously, as the acid and carbonate react together, giving off carbon dioxide. The oozing froth looks like a miniature volcanic eruption!

# ELECTRIC REACTIONS

Chemical reactions need energy to work. In the atmosphere, lightning supplies the energy for reactions between nitrogen and oxygen, present in air, to form nitrogen oxide. This combines with moisture to form nitric acid, which rain then washes into the soil. The acid combines with other substances to form salts called nitrates, which are valuable nutrients for plants. Chemists also use electricity to bring about reactions. They use it to split up chemical compounds, in a process called electrolysis. Aluminium is extracted from its ore by electrolysis.

# CHEMISTS AT WORK

**USING THEIR KNOWLEDGE OF THE CHEMICAL** elements and how they react together, chemists have developed countless useful products, such as plastics, new dyes, and new medicines. Chemists are scientists who study the properties and make-up of substances and the changes that take place in them. In two separate branches of chemistry, organic chemists study carbon and the compounds it forms, while inorganic chemists study all the other elements. Research into living things and the chemical changes that take place within them is the work of biochemists.

## FLAME TESTS

Chemists can use flame tests to identify the elements present in particular chemical samples. Because the tests involve hazardous chemicals, they are carried out under strictly controlled laboratory conditions. Scientists burn a little of each sample and note how it colours the flame. Different elements turn the flame different colours. Here, chemists burn salts (such as nitrates) of barium, copper, sodium, and lithium using methylated spirit. The salts are ground into a powder and put in separate glass dishes before methylated spirit is added and lit with a match. The colour of the flame when it touches the salt indicates which element is present in the chemical sample.

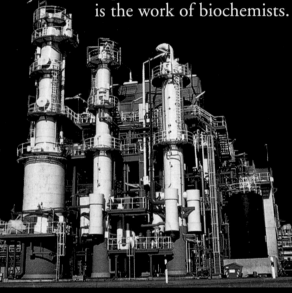

**Chemical industry**
Distillation – condensing vapours back into liquids – is a common factory process. This photograph (above) shows the distillation towers of a large chemical factory. The chemical industry produces millions of tonnes of chemicals every year, particularly acids, alkalis, and fertilizers, which are known as heavy chemicals. Chemical engineers design chemical factories and reproduce on a large scale the reactions that chemists carry out in their laboratories.

*Barium salts give the flame a greenish tinge.*

**Perkin and synthetic dye**
In 1856, the English chemistry student William Henry Perkin (1838–1907) made one of the first synthetic (artificial) dyes, mauveine. He prepared it from aniline, an organic substance in coal tar. In 1857, he built a factory to produce the vivid purple dye, and launched the organic chemical industry.

# TESTING TIMES

The analysis of chemical samples is an important part of a chemist's work. In qualitative analysis, chemists aim to find the nature of substances present in different samples. They may conduct simple tests, such as a flame test, and then carry out more systematic investigations using a range of standard chemicals and sophisticated apparatus. In quantitative analysis, chemists try to find the amounts of each substance present. They need to separate the various substances in the sample, then work out how much of each substance is present.

## LET'S EXPERIMENT
### CHROMATOGRAPHY

**CHEMISTS OFTEN USE** a technique called chromatography to separate substances from a mixture. Chromatography can be used to separate coloured dyes and pigments. **You will need:** inks or food colouring; some glass jars; blotting paper; water; bulldog clips.

**1** Mix together the inks (or food colours) in small jars, putting a different mixture into each one.

**2** Place a drop of each mixture on separate strips of blotting paper. Put a little water in some clean jars, then attach a bulldog clip to each strip of blotting paper and dangle a strip into each jar so they just dip into the water.

**3** As the water flows up through the paper, it carries the colours with it. Some colours travel faster than others, so the mixtures split into coloured bands.

*Methylated spirit by itself burns blue. This is the test flame.*

*Copper salts burn bright green.*

*Sodium salts burn a vivid yellow-orange.*

*Lithium salts burn bright red.*

# ACIDS AND BASES

## WHEN YOU BITE INTO A LEMON, IT TASTES VERY SOUR.

If you drink stale milk, you find that this tastes sour too. So does vinegar. They taste sour because they contain acids. The word acid means "sour" in Latin. The acids in lemons, sour milk, and vinegar are weak, but other acids are strong and dangerous. Car batteries contain sulphuric acid, which burns skin and attacks metals. Acids have chemical opposites, called bases. The bases that dissolve in water are called alkalis, and like acids, bases can be strong or weak. One of the strongest bases is caustic soda, a substance used in oven cleaners. It is termed caustic because it can burn flesh. Soap, on the other hand, is a weak base. Bases tend to feel soapy or slippery to the touch.

## ACID ATTACK

Sulphuric acid is one of the most common acids. When concentrated, it can burn paper and human flesh. The acid dehydrates any substance it comes into contact with. It reacts with paper (above), which contains carbon, hydrogen, and oxygen, and leaves behind black carbon. In solution, the most common acids produce electrically charged particles of hydrogen, called hydrogen ions. Scientists give these ions the symbol $H^+$ because they have a positive electric charge.

### Acid rain
When coal burns in power stations, it releases sulphur dioxide into the atmosphere. This combines with moisture in the air to form droplets of dilute sulphuric acid. When it rains, it rains acid, which can kill trees and pollute lakes and rivers.

### Weak acids
The acid that gives lemons and other citrus fruits their sharp taste is citric acid. Apples and grapes contain a lot of tartaric acid. Sour milk contains lactic acid. These organic acids are much weaker than inorganic acids, such as sulphuric acid, because they don't let go of their hydrogen ions very easily.

## ALKALIS

Lime is an alkali that can be used to treat acid in polluted water. A helicopter (left) is dropping lime onto a polluted lake in Sweden. Treating the lake with lime combats, or neutralizes, the acid in it. Lime is the compound calcium hydroxide. Like all alkalis, it produces hydroxide ions ($OH^-$) in solution. Acids can produce hydrogen ions ($H^+$). When an alkali and acid get together, the hydrogen ions and hydroxide ions combine to form water. If all the ions are used up, the final solution will be neutral – neither acidic nor alkaline.

## Sting in the tail

Bee stings are very painful. The bee injects acid into a person's flesh with its barbed sting (shown magnified above). The person who has been stung can relieve the pain after the sting has been removed by washing the wound with soap. Soap is a mild alkali that neutralizes the acid. Ants and nettles also sting with acid.

## Soothing the stomach

Sometimes when people eat very rich foods, acid builds up in their stomachs, which makes them feel uncomfortable. To relieve the symptoms of acid indigestion, sufferers can take antacid tablets. These contain a mild alkali, such as calcium carbonate, which reacts with the acid in the stomach and neutralizes it.

## LET'S EXPERIMENT
## ACID INDICATORS

**CHEMISTS USE CHEMICAL** solutions called indicators to find out whether a substance is an acid or an alkali, and also to see exactly how acidic or alkaline it is. Indicators work by changing colour. A common indicator is litmus, made from certain plants called lichens. Litmus is red in acid solutions and blue in alkaline solutions. Indicators can also be made from other plant materials. In this experiment, red cabbage is used. **You will need:** an adult present; red cabbage; knife; saucepan; a heat source; sieve; lemon juice; milk of magnesia (available from chemists); bicarbonate of soda. Do not attempt to mix the test substances used in this experiment.

**1** Chop up a red cabbage and slice it thinly. Next, heat a saucepan of clean water until it boils.

**2** Carefully add the cabbage to the boiling water. Then take the pan off the heat. Leave it to cool.

**3** Strain the cabbage through a sieve, catching the reddish-purple water in a jar. This is your indicator.

**4** Pour a little of the indicator into jars. Add the substances you want to test, and note any change in colour.

| Lemon juice | Milk of magnesia | Bicarbonate of soda |
|---|---|---|

A weak acid turns the indicator red.

A fairly strong alkali turns the indicator green.

A weak alkali turns the indicator bluish-purple.

## THE PH SCALE

How acidic or alkaline a solution is relates to the number of hydrogen ions ($H^+$) that are present. A solution with many such ions is strongly acidic. A solution with few ions is alkaline. Chemists can work out the amount of ions present using the pH scale. The letters pH stand for "power of hydrogen". On this scale, a solution with a pH of 1 is strongly acidic, and a solution with a pH of 14 is strongly alkaline. Neutral solutions, which are neither acidic nor alkaline, have a pH of 7.

*Indicator paper turns pink in dilute hydrochloric acid, which has a pH of about 1.*

| Colour changes in universal indicator paper | Hydrochloric acid pH of about 1 | Vinegar pH of about 4 | Tap water pH of about 6 | Liquid soap pH of about 8–9 | Household cleaner pH of about 10 |
|---|---|---|---|---|---|

# SALTS AND SOAPS

**WHEN YOU GO SWIMMING IN THE SEA, YOU** will notice how salty the water is. This is because the sea is full of dissolved salts. The main one is the chemical compound sodium chloride, better known as common or table salt – the ingredient we use to season our food. Salts are formed when acids react with alkalis and other bases, or when acids attack metals. Chlorides can be produced from hydrochloric acid. Sulphates can be made from sulphuric acid, and nitrates from nitric acids. Soaps and detergents are special salts that can remove grease and dirt.

*Sodium ion*   *Chloride ion*   *Ionic bond*

*Sodium chloride forms cubic crystals.*

## COMPOUND OF IONS

Most salts are ionic compounds, made up of ions (electrically charged atoms). Sodium chloride, for example, is made up of positively charged sodium ions and negatively charged chloride ions. In the solid state, the ions in salt arrange themselves into a rigid structure called a lattice. The electrical attraction between the negative and positive charges makes a bond between the ions. In water, most salts dissolve easily because the ions attract the water molecules.

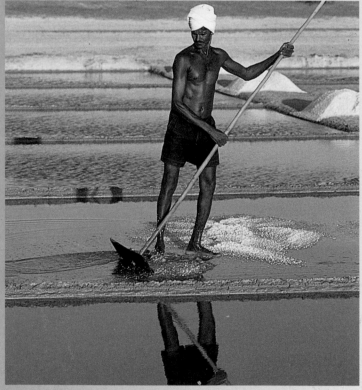

### Adding fluoride

Fluorine is one of the many minerals the human body needs to stay healthy. It helps make stronger bones and teeth. In some areas, fluoride salts are added to the drinking water to help prevent tooth decay. Fluorides are added to some toothpastes for the same reason.

### Panning for salts

Every litre of sea water holds about 25 g (1 oz) of salt. In hot climates, salt is "mined" straight from the sea. This is done by channelling sea water into shallow basins. As heat from the Sun slowly evaporates the water, the salt comes out of solution and solidifies. Elsewhere, salt is produced by mining deposits of the mineral halite (rock salt).

## ‹ SILVER SALTS ›

Certain salts of silver have the unusual property of being sensitive to light. This makes them useful in photography. The light-sensitive coating, or emulsion, on film contains silver bromide. When light falls on it, the bromide changes invisibly. Developing the film with chemicals produces a visible image. Unchanged silver bromide is then removed in a process called fixing. 114 ▶

*Here, hypo (sodium thiosulphate) is dissolving silver bromide. This process is often used in photographic processing for fixing.*

*This chalky limescale is deposited on a heating element in a hard-water area.*

## LET'S EXPERIMENT
### WATER HARDNESS

**FIND OUT HOW HARD** your tap water is by comparing it with distilled (soft) water. Soft waters contain different salts to hard waters; some soft waters contain no salts at all. **You will need**: liquid soap; distilled water; tap water; two jars with lids; eye-dropper.

**1** Mix equal amounts of liquid soap and distilled water to make a soap solution. Half-fill the jars, one with distilled water, the other with tap water.

**2** Using an eye-dropper, add soap solution to the distilled water drop by drop. Put on the lid and shake after each drop. Note how many drops are needed to make a good bubbly lather.

**3** Now add soap solution to the tap water drop by drop. Shake the jar between drops. How many drops do you need to make a good lather in the tap water as compared to the distilled water? The extra number of drops you need is a guide to the water's hardness.

## HARD WATER

When rain falls through the air, it absorbs carbon dioxide and other gases. These make the rain slightly acidic. On the ground, the acidic water dissolves rocks, especially soft rocks such as limestone. This produces salt solutions of magnesium and calcium hydrogen carbonates, which make water "hard". Hard water doesn't easily form a lather with soap. We can remove these salts from water by boiling, when they are precipitated (come out of solution) as a chalky deposit. We can also remove salts by using special water softeners.

## SOAPS AND DETERGENTS

Soap is one of the oldest types of cleaning substances. It is made by boiling animal fats or plant oils with alkalis, such as caustic soda. This produces special salts that can attack grease and dirt. The trouble is that soap reacts with the dissolved salts in hard water to form a messy scum – something often seen left in a ring around the bathtub after washing. Modern detergents are also salts, often made from petroleum chemicals and sulphuric acid. They don't form scum and have other chemicals added to improve the cleaning action.

## HOW SOAP WORKS

Soaps and detergents can lift greasy dirt from objects because they have special kinds of molecules, which have a head and a tail. The head is attracted to water – it is hydrophilic (water-loving). The tail is attracted to grease, but not to water – it is hydrophobic (water-fearing). The tails attach to the greasy dirt, surrounding it. The heads are attracted to the water and float the dirt away.

*Long, water-fearing tails of the detergent molecules are attracted to the grease on the spoon.*

*Grease particles are surrounded by detergent tails. The water-loving heads outside now pull the particles into the water.*

# CARBON CHEMISTRY

**CARBON IS ONE OF THE MOST COMMON ELEMENTS IN THE** world around us. Because carbon atoms link readily, both with each other and with other elements, they can form millions of different compounds. The variety of carbon substances found in nature ranges from carbon dioxide in the air, to diamonds, the hardest mineral on Earth. Scientists once believed that all but the simplest carbon compounds could only be produced by living organisms. They used the term "organic" to refer to carbon compounds, and the study of carbon compounds was called organic chemistry. We still use the term organic, even though synthetic carbon compounds are now commonplace.

## ELEMENT OF LIFE

Carbon is vital to all living things. For example, the sap from rubber trees (above) contains a carbon compound called isoprene ($C_5H_8$), which forms a natural plastic. Like all plants, the rubber tree absorbs carbon dioxide ($CO_2$) from the air. Plants combine carbon dioxide with water to produce carbohydrates, which are compounds of carbon, hydrogen, and oxygen. Fossil fuels, such as oil, gas, and coal, also release carbon dioxide into the air when they burn. In fact, fossil fuels are actually carbon compounds created by decayed plants and animals.

**Thermosets and thermoplastics**
This old radio is made from Bakelite, the first entirely synthetic plastic, developed in 1907. Bakelite is an example of a thermoset plastic, which sets rigid and does not melt if reheated. Polythene and nylon are examples of thermoplastics, which do melt if reheated. Plastics are very useful, but can cause a problem for the environment because the molecules do not break down and decay.

*Hydrogen atoms linked to the carbon chain*

*Carbon atoms form the backbone of a polythene polymer.*

## MOLECULE CHAINS

Most substances, such as water ($H_2O$) and carbon dioxide ($CO_2$), have small molecules that consist of a few atoms. Many carbon compounds have large molecules with carbon atoms linked together in a long chain. Chemists use the property of carbon atoms to link together in chains to make plastics, a type of synthetic carbon compound. Another name for plastics is polymers, which means "many parts". Each basic repeated unit of the chain is a monomer, which means "one part".

*The monomer ethene ($C_2H_4$) forms the basic unit of the plastic polythene.*

**Synthetic dyes**
People have always liked to dye their clothes, but were once limited in their choice of colours. They had to extract natural dyes from plants, snails, and even insects. Today, we make most dyes synthetically, using organic chemicals from oil to produce an unlimited variety of colours. Synthetic dyes are generally brighter and longer-lasting than natural dyes.

## Composites

As this pole-vaulter springs into the air, his pole bends but does not break. The pole is made of fibreglass, a type of plastic called a composite. Fibreglass contains long glass fibres that reinforce the plastic, making it particularly strong and flexible, while also being fairly light in weight. Other composites use carbon fibres for extra strength and flexibility.

## Heat-resistant carbon

Carbon has a very high melting point of 3,500°C (6,300°F), making it an ideal refractory (heat-resistant) material. In industry, carbon is used to make containers to hold molten metals. The nose and wings of the space shuttle are tipped with carbon to resist the high temperatures experienced during re-entry into Earth's atmosphere.

*Carbon protects the most vulnerable parts of the space shuttle from extreme heat.*

## LET'S EXPERIMENT
## MAKING A POLYMER SLIME

**IN THERMOPLASTICS** like PVA (polyvinyl acetate), cross-linking agents are sometimes added to bind the polymers together. In this experiment, we use a cross-linking agent to turn PVA into a lovely gooey slime. PVA's main use is in emulsion paints, in which it forms the protective film. It is also used to make glue, like the glue in this experiment. The agent we use to make the PVA cross-link is borax, used in laundry softeners. **You will need:** an adult present; PVA glue; borax powder (available from pharmacies); bowl; spoon; water. Take care – borax is a skin and eye irritant. Always wash your hands after handling the slime. This slime is not edible!

**1** In a bowl, mix together equal amounts of the PVA glue and water. Stir well. Pour some water into a separate jar and stir a tablespoon of borax powder into the water. Keep adding the borax until no more will dissolve. You now have a saturated solution.

**2** Add two tablespoons of the borax solution to the PVA mixture. Stir the new mixture quickly to combine all of the substances. The mixture should become thicker as the borax begins working as a cross-linking agent. The borax binds together the long-chain polymers of the PVA, thickening the liquid mixture and turning it into wonderful slime!

*If you add more borax solution to the PVA mixture, it will become more solid, like putty.*

### The synthesis of urea

In 1828, a German chemist named Friedrich Wöhler produced a synthetic substance that had previously only been found in living things. He boiled a solution of ammonia and a cyanide salt to make urea, the main substance in animal urine. It was the first organic compound created artificially from inorganic chemicals. Since Wöhler's discovery, scientists have synthesized many carbon compounds, including paints, dyes, plastics, flavourings, detergents, and drugs.

**Friedrich Wöhler (1800–82)**

# THE SCIENCE OF LIFE

**OUR PLANET TEEMS WITH LIFE. WE KNOW OF MILLIONS** of different species (kinds) of plants, animals, and other living things, such as bacteria and fungi. All these organisms have certain things in common. They take in (eat) raw materials, they obtain energy from the raw materials, they get rid of the waste, and they reproduce (produce offspring similar to themselves). All life is made up of cells – from the smallest insect to the largest tree. Cells are the building blocks of living things and are like tiny chemical factories, producing the substances that make living things work.

## SINGLE-CELL LIFE

The simplest life-forms consist of organisms with single cells. The plant-like organisms called algae are made up of single cells with nuclei (centres). Like plants, algae contain green chlorophyll, a vital substance that allows them to make their food by photosynthesis. The microscopic algae known as *Volvox* (below) are made up of loose colonies of simple cells. Hundreds of identical simple cells are arranged on the outside of round balls.

## HOW LIFE BEGAN

No one really knows how life on Earth began. Many scientists believe that life began in a "soup" of organic chemicals in the oceans, produced by reactions between gases in the early atmosphere. Later, other reactions in the oceans produced more complex molecules that could reproduce themselves. However, some astronomers believe that comets like Hale-Bopp (below) may have carried the simple organic compounds to Earth. Traces of such organic matter have already been detected in comets.

**Cells and tissues**
More complex animals are made up of many different kinds of cells – a human body contains over 200 kinds. Human nerve cells (above-left) are cable-like structures which link all the body parts to the brain and the spinal cord. Cells group together to form different kinds of tissues, depending on their function.

## Bacteria

This highly magnified salmonella bacterium can cause food poisoning. Bacteria are by far the most common life form on Earth – there are billions in your body alone. They are a very simple life form, usually consisting of just one single cell, with no nucleus.

# DEMONSTRATING
## HOW PLANTS MAKE FOOD

**PHOTOSYNTHESIS IS THE PROCESS** by which green plants use the energy in sunlight to make their food from water and carbon dioxide. Food is stored in their leaves as starch. This demonstration shows how plants need light to make their food, using iodine to test for starch. It must be done by an adult in a lab, as methylated spirit is highly flammable.

**The demonstrator will need:** plant; methylated spirit; hot plate; pan; iodine solution; dropper; heat-resistant beaker; scissors; black plastic; tape; petri dish; tweezers.

**1** Some of the plant's leaves are wrapped in black plastic and left in the light for 2 days. Two leaves are then picked: one that has been covered and one that hasn't.

**2** 100ml (3.4 fl.oz) methylated spirit is placed in a heatproof beaker. This is stood in a pan of water and heated until the spirit boils. The pan and beaker are removed from the heat. Using tweezers, each leaf is carefully dropped into the boiling water for 1 minute, and then into the beaker of methylated spirits, and left until they are almost white.

**3** Each leaf is placed on a petri dish and a few drops of iodine added. The leaf exposed to light will turn dark – it contains starch as photosynthesis has taken place. The covered-up leaf will not turn dark because it contains no starch – no light reached it so photosynthesis didn't take place.

*Normal leaf*    *Leaf kept in dark*    *Leaf in light*

A model of a short section of human DNA

# DNA

Inside the nucleus of your cells is a very important molecule. It is known as DNA, which is short for deoxyribonucleic acid. DNA carries all the chemical instructions that tell cells how to work, for example how to make the proteins that keep the body alive and growing. DNA is found in long, thread-like packages called chromosomes. Humans normally have 23 pairs of chromosomes. They carry all the characteristics, or genes, that make you different from everybody else on Earth.

*Pituitary gland*

## Human chemistry

Chemical reactions take place in our bodies all the time. Oxidation takes place in our cells as the oxygen in the air we breathe combines with carbon in the food we eat. This produces the energy we need to live. In digestion, chemical enzymes help break down foods for the body to absorb. Our glands produce hormones, which are chemical messengers that help control the body. The pituitary gland is the hormone "headquarters" of the body. Hormones released from here are able to instruct other hormone-making glands what to do.

# FORCES AND ENERGY

**Picture:** *The cue ball slams into a pack of pool balls, transferring its energy to them.*

# FORCES AND ENERGY

**ENERGY IS ALL AROUND US – IT POURS**
down on to Earth from the Sun as heat
and light. It is stored in our fuels and
released when they burn. We use
many different forms of energy in
many different ways – for example,
to heat our homes, drive our
machines, and send space probes to
alien worlds. Whenever energy is
used to make something happen,
forces come into play. We can think
of forces as being the means by which
energy is applied. They are the pushes
and pulls that get things moving.
Without energy and forces, nothing
would happen in our world or indeed
in the Universe.

## ENERGY SOURCES

Three main substances provide us with
energy in our everyday lives – oil, natural
gas, and coal. They are fuels, which we
burn to produce energy. We call them fossil
fuels because they are the remains of
ancient plants and animals. These

*Nuclear power stations, such as this one in
France, harness the energy locked up in atoms.*

organisms grew by
harnessing the energy from the
Sun, and when they died, this energy
remained stored inside them. Today, we are
beginning to harness solar energy directly,
with solar heating panels and solar cells.
Solar energy is a source of energy that will
never run out. We call it a renewable
resource. Scientists and engineers are
developing other renewable resources to
keep the world supplied with energy when
the fossil fuels run out. They include wind,
water, and wave power.

## ENERGY CONVERSIONS

Energy can be converted from one form to
another. The energy in fuels is stored
within the chemicals they contain. When
we burn them, we break down the

*The chemical energy in the
rockets bursts out as light,
sound, and heat energy in
this fireworks display.*

chemicals and release
the stored energy as heat.
The chemical energy is
converted into heat energy.
We can use the heat energy to
boil water into steam, and then
use the steam to spin turbines. The
heat energy is converted into mechanical
energy – the energy of motion. In turn, we
can use the turbine to spin a generator,

*The cells on this solar panel convert the energy in
sunlight into electricity.*

c. 350 BC Greek philosopher Aristotle argues that falling bodies fall at the same rate, but thinks heavy bodies fall faster than light ones.

c. 250 BC Greek mathematician Archimedes studies simple machines, such as the lever and screw.

c. 100 BC Roman engineer Vitruvius develops the water wheel for power production.

1590 Italian scientist Galileo proves all falling bodies accelerate at the same rate and later investigates pendulum laws.

1687 English physicist and mathematician Isaac Newton publishes the *Principia*, describing the laws of motion and the nature of gravity.

which makes electricity. The mechanical energy is converted into electrical energy. We can now convert electricity back into other forms of energy – into mechanical energy to drive machines; into heat in an electric fire; or into light in a light bulb.

## ENERGY CONSERVATION

Almost every form of energy can be changed into other forms in a similar way. But whenever one form of energy changes into another, the total amount of energy remains the same. There is the same amount of energy after a change as there was before. No energy has been created or destroyed. This leads us to one of nature's basic laws, the law of the conservation of energy. This states that energy can be neither created nor destroyed, only changed in form. Strictly speaking, this law doesn't seem to apply to nuclear reactions, when vast amounts of energy appear to be created. But this happens because some matter changes into energy. The equivalence of mass and energy – that they are two aspects of the same thing – is explained by Einstein's Special Theory of Relativity.

## FORCES AND MOTION

Energy, in its many different forms, is used to make things happen in our world – to drive a machine, to spin a pinwheel, to kick a ball. Whenever energy is used, forces are involved. Forces get things moving and change the way they move. The science of how forces affect movement is described by three laws of motion. These laws form the basis of a branch of physics called mechanics, which deals with the way objects move and interact with each other. The laws of motion generally account for the behaviour of all moving bodies in our everyday world, from the collisions of snooker balls to the acceleration of space rockets against the pull of the Earth's gravity. But these laws break down when dealing with atoms.

*Powered by the force of gravity, a roller coaster gathers speed as it descends.*

## FUNDAMENTAL FORCES

Gravity is not just something that happens on the Earth. It happens all over the Universe. The Sun and other stars have gravity, and the galaxies have gravity. Anything with mass has gravity. In fact gravity is a fundamental (basic) force of the Universe, which acts over vast distances. It is one of four fundamental forces, or interactions, in nature. The others are the electromagnetic force, strong force, and weak force. These three

forces act only over short distances. The electromagnetic force accounts for the electric and magnetic interaction between bodies. For example, it causes opposite electric charges or opposite magnetic poles to attract one another. The other two forces act only within the nucleus of atoms. The strong force acts between the nuclear particles and binds them together. There is also a weak force, which allows nuclear particles to change and helps explain how an atom can become radioactive.

## QUANTUM MECHANICS

Inside atoms, the everyday rules of mechanics don't apply. The particles interact with one another and move about in quite different ways from, say, the balls shooting about on a snooker table. The science that seeks to describe how particles behave within atoms is known as quantum mechanics. It takes as its starting point the fact that energy at the atomic level comes in the form of little "packets", or quanta (singular "quantum"). And it considers that particles sometimes behave as waves.

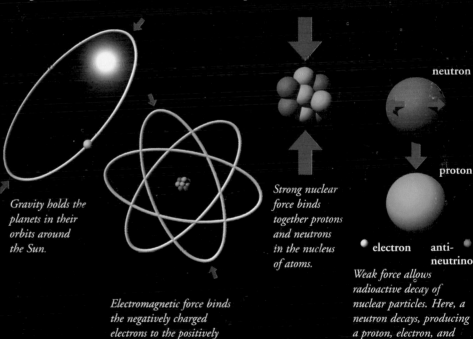

*Gravity holds the planets in their orbits around the Sun.*

*Electromagnetic force binds the negatively charged electrons to the positively charged nucleus in an atom.*

*Strong nuclear force binds together protons and neutrons in the nucleus of atoms.*

neutron

proton

electron     anti-neutrino

*Weak force allows radioactive decay of nuclear particles. Here, a neutron decays, producing a proton, electron, and an antineutrino.*

# FORCES AND MOTION

**WHEN YOU PUT A BALL ON LEVEL GROUND AND**
leave it, the ball will stay where it is. Only when you
apply a force, such as a kick, will the ball start to move.
It will then carry on moving until another force acts
upon it, for example when it hits a wall. The way
that the ball behaves is the result of one of the most
important laws of physics, first described by the English
scientist, Isaac Newton, more than 300 years ago.
Newton summed up his ideas about forces and
movement in his three laws of motion. The first law
is sometimes called the law of inertia. Inertia is the
property of matter that makes a body – in this
case a ball – resist a change in motion.

## INERTIA

At the beginning of a game of snooker, the red balls
are placed together in the shape of a triangle. If they
are left alone, they will not move because their inertia
keeps them where they are. They stay put until the cue
ball hits them and provides the force to make them
move. The cue ball travels in a straight line until it is
acted on by a force – the force of hitting another ball.

## MASS AND MOMENTUM

Once a body is set moving, it has kinetic energy,
which is the energy of motion. A measure of its energy
is its momentum, which equals mass multiplied by
speed. The more massive (heavy) a body is and the
greater its speed, the greater is its momentum. A
moving car has great momentum, and when it hits
something, its momentum tries to keep it moving.
A powerful force is created that can crumple the steel
body and throw the passengers forwards in the crash.
This is why the occupants must wear seat belts.

**Isaac
Newton
(1642–1727)**

**Newton's laws of motion**
Put simply, Newton's first law says that
an object speeds up or slows down only
when a force acts on it. According to
the second law, the amount by which
an object changes speed (acceleration)
depends on its mass and how big the
force is. The third law states that
whenever a forces acts, an equal
force acts in the opposite direction.

## LET'S EXPERIMENT
### INERTIA

**WITH A LITTLE HELP FROM INERTIA,** you can remove a cloth from a table
without touching the objects on top of it. **You will need:** an adult present;
cloth without a hem; plastic tableware. Do not use the best china!

**1** Lay the cloth on the table and place
the objects on it. Hold the end of
the cloth with both hands and give a
really sharp horizontal tug.

**2** With practice, you should be able
to whisk away the cloth and leave the
objects where they were. Their inertia
stops them from moving with the cloth.

# ACTION AND REACTION

Rocket engines like those of the *Saturn V* Moon rocket (above) work on the principle of Newton's third law of motion. Fuel burns inside a rocket's combustion (burning) chamber to produce hot gases, and these gases shoot backwards out of the engine nozzle at high speed. The action (force) of them shooting backwards sets up a reaction (equal force in the opposite direction) that propels the rocket forwards. New rocket engines are coming into use that are propelled by ions (charged particles) instead of hot gases. Such engines also work according to Newton's third law of motion regarding action and reaction.

## LET'S EXPERIMENT
### BUILDING A ROCKET

**YOU CAN MAKE** a rocket that is propelled by water using a plastic bottle. **You will need:** an adult present; small plastic soft-drink bottle; large piece of card; scissors; glue for paper; superglue; drill and bit; cork; needle adaptor for inflating footballs; old rubber glove; water; foot pump and connector.

**1** Ask an adult to drill a small hole through the cork. Push the needle adaptor through the hole, ensuring a tight fit. Also check that the cork fits the bottle tightly. If necessary, fit a rubber sleeve (cut from the finger of an old rubber glove) around the cork.

**2** Make some fins from card. They will hold up the rocket's base and help it to fly straight. Cut out a rough fin shape from a piece of card with a flap at the top and middle to fit the shape of the upturned bottle. Use this fin as a template to make two more. To strengthen the fins, cut smaller fin shapes, fold, and then glue them to the fins. Ask an adult to superglue the three fins at equal distances around the bottle.

**3** Quarter-fill the bottle with water, and push in the cork. Then connect the foot pump to the adaptor. Your rocket is now ready for blast-off. Take it outside, away from buildings and overhead cables, and stand it on its fins on a flat surface.

*Blast-off! The rocket lifts off, propelled by a jet of water and air.*

**4** Keeping your distance, start slowly pumping air into the bottle using the foot pump. The air pressure inside the bottle will build up until the cork pops out (the connector might backlash). The water and air shoot out at high speed, propelling the rocket into the air. The action of the water and air escaping backwards creates a reaction in the opposite direction, which propels the rocket upwards. This demonstrates Newton's third law of motion.

*The fins support the rocket and keep it steady on the launch pad.*

# FRICTION

**IF YOU PLACE A BLOCK OF WOOD ON THE GROUND AND GIVE IT A**
push, it doesn't move very far before it stops. Some kind of force must
have stopped it, otherwise it would have continued moving for ever. The
block's movement was stopped by friction, a force that acts between any
two surfaces rubbing together. The rougher the surfaces, the greater the
friction, because the raised bits on rough surfaces keep catching one
another. The friction, or rubbing between surfaces, produces energy
in the form of heat. That is why we rub our hands together on
cold days to make them warm up.

## HOT STUFF

When you strike a match against a rough surface, the
friction produces heat. The heat triggers off chemical
reactions in the substances that coat the match head,
which cause the match to burst into flame. "Strike-
anywhere" matches ignite when struck on any
surface. Safety matches ignite only
when struck on a special surface.

## LET'S EXPERIMENT
## MAKING A MINI HOVERCRAFT

**HOVERCRAFT REST ON A "CUSHION" OF AIR.** This reduces
friction, enabling high speeds. In this experiment, a glass
becomes a hovercraft. The air cushion is formed by warm air
escaping from the glass. **You will need:** a glass; washing-up
liquid; hot tap water; a smooth surface (such as a tray).

**1** Wash up a glass in hot soapy
water and place it upside-
down on a wet, smooth surface.

**2** Give the glass a little push. It
will slide easily as the warm
air escapes beneath it.

### Hovercraft

In a hovercraft, a powerful fan
pumps air under the hull to create
an air cushion. A flexible "skirt"
around the bottom helps keep the
air in. The craft is driven by
spinning propellers at the rear. It is
steered by moving flaps in the air
stream coming from the propellers.

## ON YOUR BIKE!

The bicycle is one of the most efficient
machines ever invented. It evolved
into its modern form in 1885, when
Englishman John Starley built his safety
bicycle. It had two equal-sized wheels,
central cranks and pedals, and a chain
driving the rear wheel. Friction governs
the working of a bicycle. Without
friction, the wheels wouldn't grip the
road and the rider's feet wouldn't grip
the pedals. The rider would have no
means of stopping because brakes rely
on friction to work. In the moving parts,
however, friction needs to be reduced so
that they can move more easily. Oil and
grease provide the answer. They help
keep the moving metal surfaces apart.

*Grease lubricates the chain
and reduces friction.*

*Friction between tyre and
road allows the wheel to
roll over the ground
without sliding.*

*Brakes force pads against the wheel rim, creating friction that slows down the wheel.*

*Grease reduces friction in the wheel bearings and allows the wheel to turn more smoothly.*

*The shape of a fish's body reduces drag.*

# STREAMLINING

Fluids (liquids and gases) cause friction too. Boats travelling through the water experience resistance, or drag, caused by water molecules rubbing against the hull. Planes experience drag because of friction with air molecules. Drag is reduced if the moving body has a smooth surface and is properly shaped, or streamlined. Fish are beautifully streamlined and travel through water with the least resistance.

*Tread allows water to escape beneath the tyre. A layer of water reduces friction, but makes it more difficult for the tyre to grip the road.*

# SPEED AND ACCELERATION

IF YOU WALK BRISKLY, YOU MIGHT BE ABLE TO COVER a distance of about 4 km (2.5 miles) in an hour. During this time you would have been moving at a speed of 4 kmh (2.5 mph). Speed is the distance travelled divided by the time taken. Often, in science, we talk about velocity rather than speed. Velocity is speed in a particular direction. So even if the speed stays constant, if the direction changes, so does the velocity. However, speeds are rarely kept constant, things are always speeding up or slowing down. When something speeds up, we say it accelerates. When it slows down, we say it decelerates.

*Laser light being used to carry signals in a laboratory experiment*

## SPEED OF LIGHT

During a storm, lightning and thunder happen at nearly the same time, but the lightning flash is seen seconds before the thunder is heard. This is because light travels faster than sound. Scientists have found that light travels at the incredible speed of about 300,000 km (186,000 miles) a second, or more than 1 billion kmh (600 million mph). They tell us that this is the highest speed anything can ever reach.

## SPEED OF SOUND

When a rifle fires a bullet, a loud bang is heard. It is the noise of the shock waves made by the bullet travelling faster than the speed of sound. Sound travels through the air at a speed of about 1,200 kmh (750 mph). Bullets travel at more than twice this speed. Sound travels much faster in solid objects than it does in air. In steel, it travels at a speed of over 16,000 kmh (10,000 mph). But sound has zero speed in a vacuum. It can't travel where there are no molecules of matter to carry it.

### Speedometers

A speedometer displays a car's speed. It is usually driven by a cable from the car's gearbox. Inside the speedometer, the cable turns a magnet, which drags with it a metal cap attached to the pointer. A spring opposes the cap's movement and makes the pointer stop at a certain position. This position corresponds to the car's speed and is read by the driver in either kilometres or miles per hour.

### G-force acceleration

When you get in a lift and it starts to rise, you feel your feet pressing harder against the floor. It's as though you have suddenly got heavier or that gravity has suddenly increased. What you are experiencing is what astronauts call a G-force. It is an extra gravity-like force on your body brought about by the acceleration of the lift upwards. Space shuttle astronauts experience forces of up to 4 Gs (four times normal gravity) when they are launched, accelerating from 0 to over 28,000 kmh (17,500 mph) in less than nine minutes.

*Increasing G-forces push the astronaut back in his seat as he accelerates.*

*When the astronaut suddenly stops, even bigger G forces throw him forwards.*

*In training, astronauts experience G-forces in a centrifuge. They are whirled round at high speed in a gondola on the end of a long arm.*

### Dragster deceleration

Dragsters reach high speeds, but they don't have very good brakes! They often use parachutes to help them slow down, or decelerate. The parachutes are deployed (opened) at the rear. As they billow out, they catch the air and force the dragster to slow down. Note the short wings, or aerofoils, at the front and back of this car. They are angled into the airstream to produce forces that press down on the car to help stop it lifting.

# BUILT FOR ACCELERATION

Drag racing is one of the most exciting types of motor racing. Two long cars, called dragsters, with huge exposed engines, battle it out on a traditional quarter-mile track to see which can accelerate the fastest. Some dragsters can cover the distance in less than 5 seconds, reaching speeds of over 460 kmh (290 mph). The powerful engines drive the big, broad, rear wheels. The spinning of these wheels tends to make the front of the dragster lift, so it is built with a long body to counter this effect. In the dragster below, the central position of the engines helps too.

# GRAVITY, MASS, AND WEIGHT

**WHEN YOU DROP SOMETHING, IT FALLS BECAUSE AN** invisible force is pulling it – the force of gravity, or rather Earth's gravity. Gravity is a basic property of all matter, from atoms to planets. The more mass a body has, the stronger its gravity. The English scientist Isaac Newton was the first to understand the nature of gravity in the 1660s. It is said that watching falling apples triggered off his ideas. Gravity gives bodies their weight. Weight is the force a body experiences because of its mass in the presence of gravity.

## FALLING BODIES

Gravity acts between bodies and pulls them together. If the bodies are different masses, the uneven pull makes the smaller mass fall towards the larger mass. We notice this on Earth when objects fall downwards – towards the massive planet. About 400 years ago, the Italian scientist Galileo decided to experiment with falling bodies. He found that gravity causes everything to fall at the same rate. Light bodies fall as quickly as heavy bodies. So in a vacuum (to avoid air resistance), a feather falls as fast as an apple (right).

### Free fall
To start with, gravity pulls free-fall parachutists towards Earth at ever-increasing speeds. But the faster they fall, the more air resistance they experience. When they reach about 300 kmh (190 mph), air resistance becomes so high that it balances the pull of gravity. They then continue to fall steadily at this speed, which is called the terminal velocity.

### Zero-g
Astronauts in orbit around Earth feel as if their bodies have no weight. It seems as if gravity no longer exists. We call this peculiar state weightlessness or zero-g. But the proper name for it is continuous free fall. Gravity does still exist in orbit (it's only five per cent less than on the Earth's surface) and is making them fall to Earth. Because their space shuttle is travelling forwards so fast, the amount they fall towards Earth in any time equals the amount the Earth's surface curves away beneath them. Therefore they stay at the same height above Earth, even though they are falling.

## Moon and tides

The Moon has a much smaller mass than Earth, and its gravity is only one-sixth as strong. Nevertheless, its pull still affects our planet. As it orbits Earth, it tugs at the water in the oceans and creates high and low tides. Some land masses, such as the one below, are joined to the mainland at low tide, but become islands at high tide.

Mont St Michel, France.

# GRAVITY GONE MAD

When a large star dies, it blasts itself apart as a supernova, the biggest explosion in the Universe. The matter in its core (centre) collapses so rapidly that it releases a huge amount of energy, causing the blast. What's left of the core gets crushed smaller and smaller. The smaller and denser the core gets, the stronger its gravity becomes. Eventually, the core is crushed almost to nothing, leaving only a region of space with enormous gravity. We call this region a black hole because we can never see it – not even light rays escape from its gravitational grip.

## LET'S EXPERIMENT
### CENTRE OF GRAVITY

**IN ANY OBJECT,** all the weight appears to be concentrated at one point. We call it the centre of gravity (or centre of mass). As you will see in this experiment, if you support an object beneath its centre of gravity, it will balance. **You will need:** pencil; piece of card; scissors; pin; a board (such as a cork board, in a vertical position); cotton thread; a weight.

*Make the weight heavy enough to pull the thread taut.*

**1** Draw an outline of your hand on the card and cut it out. Pin the card hand to the board by the tip of one finger so that the hand swings freely. Hang a weighted thread from the pin and draw along the line of the thread on the card. Repeat using the rest of the fingers. Be careful not to prick yourself with the pin.

*Balance the hand on a pencil.*

**2** You should find that all the lines you drew on the hand meet at one point. This is the centre of gravity. Place the end of the pencil beneath the point, and you should find that the hand balances.

# SWINGING AND SPINNING

**A PLAYGROUND IS THE PERFECT PLACE TO** investigate swinging and spinning. The swings show pendulum laws, and the roundabout shows circular motion. Time how long it takes you to swing back and forth on both huge and tiny swings. Surprisingly, you'll find that the swing always moves back and forth in more or less the same time. The Italian scientist Galileo Galilei (1564–1642) noticed this in the 1580s when he experimented with pendulums. He found that pendulums of the same length always have the same period (time of swing). Try also spinning on a roundabout. A force acting inwards keeps you travelling in a circle. The faster you spin, the stronger the force pulls you towards its centre.

*This pendulum clock was built in 1883 to Galileo's design.*

## PENDULUMS

Galileo realised that the constant period of swing of a pendulum could be used to regulate clocks. But he died before his design could be built. The first pendulum clock was built in 1657 by the Dutch scientist Christiaan Huygens. In this, each swing released an escape wheel, tooth by tooth, which drove the clockwork mechanism. Grandfather, or long-case, clocks have a "seconds" pendulum 1 m (3 ft 3 in) long, which swings from one side to the other in exactly one second.

## LET'S EXPERIMENT
### PENDULUM SWINGS

**PENDULUMS HANG FROM A FIXED POINT** and swing under the action of gravity. Below are some pendulum investigations for you to try.
**You will need:** string; two vertical supports (such as clamp stands or chairs); a ruler; scissors; 6 identical weights (such as nuts or lumps of modelling clay); a stopwatch.

**1** Secure each end of a 1-m (3-ft 3-in) length of string to vertical supports. Stretch the string taut. Your pendulums will hang from this.

**2** Cut three different lengths of string. Fix a weight to each and hang them from the taut string. Set one swinging. Time 20 complete swings (back and forth) and divide by 20 to get an accurate time for one swing. Repeat with the other two pendulums. You should find that the different lengths have different swing times. Try adding extra weights to the pendulums and timing them. Compare your results. Do the weights affect the swing times?

**3** Now make your three pendulums the same length, and hang one weight from each. Set one swinging. You'll find that the others start swinging too. This effect is called resonance and occurs when identical objects all vibrate at their natural frequency.

### Out of balance
When designing structures, engineers must ensure that all the forces balance. The Leaning Tower of Pisa, in Italy, started leaning soon after building began. The ground began to sink on one side, creating an unbalanced force. Its centre of gravity has so far stayed within its base. At present it is being stabilised at an angle 5 degrees out of vertical. If its centre of gravity moves outside the base, a turning force will be created and the tower will fall.

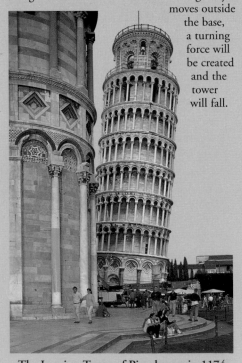

The Leaning Tower of Pisa, begun in 1174

# CIRCLING AND SPINNING

On some fairground rides, you are whirled round in circles. Your body wants to shoot off in a straight line, but is held back by a force acting inwards towards the centre of the circle. We call it centripetal force. When satellites orbit the Earth, gravity provides the centripetal force to keep them circling. Like everything that moves, spinning objects have momentum to keep them in motion. With spinning objects, it is called angular momentum.

**Conserving momentum**
Skaters often perform spectacular spins. They start spinning with their arms outstretched. This gives them a larger spin diameter and more angular momentum. By suddenly pulling in their arms, they reduce their diameter. To conserve angular momentum, their bodies automatically spin faster.

*Spinning rotor*

*Outer gimbal*

*Supporting frame*

**Gyroscopes**
Gyroscopes are amazing things. They can balance on a piece of string or on the tip of a pencil, and if you push them, they don't fall over. They have these unusual properties because of their rapidly spinning wheel, or rotor, which spins inside pivoting frames, or gimbals. When the rotor spins quickly, its angular momentum, which acts along the rotor axis, tries to keep it pointing in the same direction.

## LET'S EXPERIMENT
### CENTRIPETAL FORCE

**CAN YOU TURN A BUCKET** of water upside-down without the water falling out? You can with the help of centripetal force.
**You will need:** an adult present; strong string; scissors; a light plastic bucket; water; a jug; a glove (optional).

**1** Tie one end of the string to the handle of the bucket. Quarter-fill the bucket with water. Any more water will make the bucket too heavy.

**2** Take the bucket outdoors. For comfort perhaps wear a glove, then wind the string around your hand. Start swinging the bucket in a circle around your hand. Once the bucket is circling, centripetal force will hold the water inside.

# INVESTIGATING ENERGY

WHEN A RUBBER BAND IS STRETCHED, THEN RELEASED, IT shoots through the air. Stretching it builds up energy inside the rubber band. This energy is called potential energy. When the rubber band is released, it moves. Its potential energy is converted into the energy of movement, or kinetic energy. Potential and kinetic are the two main forms of energy. Potential energy is the energy stored in something because of its position or state. Gravitational energy, chemical energy, nuclear energy, and electrical energy are all forms of potential energy. Kinetic energy is the energy of motion. Every moving body has kinetic energy.

## FUEL AND POWER

Most of the energy we use comes from burning fossil fuels, such as oil (below), coal, and natural gas. These fuels have formed naturally over millions of years, but are being used up very quickly – oil will probably run out later this century. Burning fossil fuels also causes air pollution. Our other main energy sources are hydroelectricity (water power) and nuclear power. Nuclear power stations currently produce energy by fission, or splitting atoms. The problem is this produces lots of harmful radioactive waste.

*Towers at an oil refinery venting off waste gases.*

### Renewable resources
Some energy sources will never run out. These everlasting, or renewable, resources include flowing water and the wind. We harness flowing water in hydroelectric plants, and harness the wind with windmills. Modern windmills, called wind turbines, are now being used to generate electricity. Solar energy and geothermal energy are two other useful renewable resources now being exploited. Geothermal energy is the heat found in underground rocks, particularly in volcanic regions.

A wind farm in California, USA

### Energy without end
A machine called JET (Joint European Torus) creates a ring of searing hot gas called plasma during experiments into nuclear fusion. Unlike fission, this kind of nuclear reaction doesn't produce deadly radiation. It is the process that stars use to make their energy. If fusion can be controlled, the world will have plenty of energy because the oceans are full of the "fuel" it uses, deuterium (a heavy form of hydrogen).

## LET'S EXPERIMENT
### ENERGY CONVERSION

**LIFTING AN OBJECT GIVES IT MORE** gravitational potential energy. In letting it go, the "potential" energy is converted into kinetic energy as it falls under the pull of gravity. This is how a roller coaster works. See for yourself by making a mini roller coaster.

**You will need:** foam pipe lagging (wide enough for a marble to slide down easily); marbles; scissors; all-purpose glue; tape; two vertical supports (such as chairs); adhesive putty; pins.

**1** Cut the lagging in half lengthways with some scissors, parallel to its existing slit. Stick or tape the two pieces together end to end. Bend the track as shown in the picture. Rest it on a surface, propping it up against two vertical supports. Hold it in place by pinning to mounds of adhesive putty.

**2** Place a marble on the steep drop of the track and let it go. Find the best starting height by experiment. If too high, the marble will have too much kinetic energy and fly off the track. If too low it won't have enough energy to roll over the hump.

**A roller coaster ride**
On a roller coaster, the cars climb to the highest point under power, and are then let loose to descend under gravity. They gain increasing kinetic energy as they fall, which takes them up and over a series of lower humps.

"The Big One" roller coaster in Blackpool, England.

**Einstein's famous formula**
Early last century, Albert Einstein realised that mass and energy are related. Mass can be changed into energy, according to his famous equation $E=mc^2$. $E$ is the energy produced when a mass $m$ is converted into energy, and $c$ is the speed of light. Squaring $c$ (multiplying it by itself) gives a huge number, so a tiny amount of mass can be converted into a huge amount of energy.

$$E = mc^2$$

## SAVING ENERGY

The industrialised world uses vast amounts of energy in industry, transport, and in the home. But much of it is wasted. For example, much of the energy we use for home heating is wasted when heat escapes through the roof, walls, and windows. As our fuel supplies dwindle, we should be saving more energy. One example would be to improve insulation in our houses. Another way to save energy is by re-using, or recycling materials, like metals and glass. Recycling requires much less energy than extracting substances from raw materials.

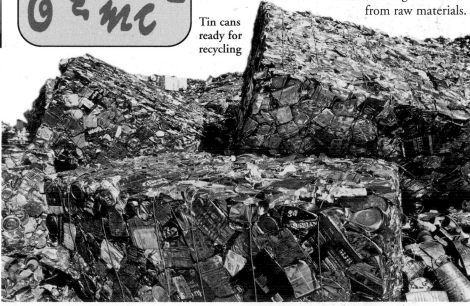

Tin cans ready for recycling

## CHAINS OF ENERGY

Logs burn vigorously on a bonfire, throwing out energy in the form of light (seen as flames) and heat. Energy can't be made or destroyed, it can only be converted from one form to another. So where did all this energy come from? It was chemical energy, stored in the molecules of the wood. This chemical energy was converted from the energy in sunlight. The leaves of the tree used sunlight, in a process called photosynthesis, to manufacture the materials needed for the tree to grow.

# ENERGY AND WORK

## SCIENTISTS DEFINE ENERGY AS THE ABILITY TO DO WORK.

But they don't mean work in the everyday meaning of the word. Instead they say work is done whenever a force moves an object. The work done is calculated by multiplying the distance the object has moved by the force needed to move it. So moving a heavy object a short distance could involve the same amount of work, and use the same energy, as moving a lighter object a longer distance. This relationship is used by machines, to make work easier to perform.

*As the wedge slices down, its widening shape creates a large sideways force that splits the wood.*

*This mountain road is an inclined plane. Cars travel a longer distance, but with less effort than climbing straight up the mountain.*

*The screw thread is like an inclined plane wrapped round the screw. The path is longer so the effort is reduced.*

*To turn this wheel, a small force can travel a long distance at the rim, or a larger force can travel a shorter distance at the axle (centre).*

## SIMPLE MACHINES

Any device that performs work is called a machine. They can often be very simple. A crowbar, for example, is a type of machine called a lever. Other simple machines include the inclined plane, wedge, screw, wheel and axle, and pulley. Most machines magnify the force applied to them (the effort) to shift a larger force (the load). When they magnify a force, they give what is called a mechanical advantage. But to get this advantage, the effort must move a long distance to shift the load a little.

What's the advantage?

Can you lift a car on your own? You can with a screwjack. This is a lifting device that uses the principles of the screw and the lever. By turning the jack handle a long way (lots of leverage), you make the screw move upwards a short way, lifting the weight of the car. The jack produces a big force for a small effort – it has a large mechanical advantage.

*Screwjack*

# LET'S EXPERIMENT
## WITH LEVERS

**THE LIDS OF PAINT TINS** fit tightly to prevent spillage. They can be opened with a lever, using the edge of the tin as a fulcrum (pivot). **You will need:** a tin of paint (ask permission); a coin; an old teaspoon; an old dessert spoon; a screwdriver; old newspaper.

**1** Rest the paint tin on some old newspaper (in case the paint spills). Try to lever off the lid with a coin. Because the coin is so short, you can't get much leverage to magnify the effort you apply. However hard you try, you can't overcome the force that keeps the lid shut.

**2** Now try opening the lid with the teaspoon, the dessert spoon, and the screwdriver. You'll find that the longer the lever is, the easier it is to open the tin. You apply less effort, but your hand has to move much further to produce enough force to lift the lid.

# LAWS OF THE LEVER

The Greek scientist Archimedes worked out the laws of the lever more than 2,000 years ago. For a simple lever resting on a fulcrum (pivot), the lifting effort multiplied by its distance to the fulcrum equals the load multiplied by its distance to the fulcrum. So a small effort applied a long way from the fulcrum can lift a large load that is close to the fulcrum. This set-up produces a large mechanical advantage – it gives you good leverage. Said Archimedes: "Give me a leverage point and I will move the world".

### First-class lever

A simple lever like a seesaw is known as a first-class lever. It has a fulcrum in the middle, the effort is applied on one side, and the load is lifted on the other. Pliers are another first-class lever. They have a mechanical advantage because the handles are longer than the jaws.

*Effort*
*Load*
*Effort*
*Fulcrum*

### Second-class lever

A second-class lever has the load positioned between the effort and the fulcrum. Because the effort is further from the fulcrum than the load, mechanical advantage is achieved. A nutcracker is a second-class lever, and so is a wheelbarrow.

*Fulcrum*
*Effort*
*Load*
*Effort*

### Third-class lever

In a third-class lever, the effort is applied between the fulcrum and the load. The effort is closer to the fulcrum than the load, so there is no mechanical advantage here. Instead, third-class levers are used whenever a delicate grip is required, for example when using chopsticks.

*Effort*
*Fulcrum*
*Load*
*Effort*

### Prime movers

All machines need energy to perform work. Some machines convert energy directly into mechanical motion. We call them prime movers. Petrol engines and steam locomotives are examples; they harness the energy in petrol and steam. Prime movers are not very efficient – they supply much less energy than they take in. Petrol engines produce only 25 per cent of the energy in their fuel; the rest is lost as heat.

# GEARS AND PULLEYS

**WHEN YOU RIDE YOUR BIKE, A SET OF GEARS** transmits the motion of the pedals to the rear wheel. In a car (or other motorised vehicle), gears transmit power from the engine to the wheels to make the car go. Most gears take the form of wheels with teeth cut around the edge. Gears not only transmit motion, they can also change it. Using the gears on your bike, you can change speed while still pedalling at the same rate, thereby gaining a mechanical advantage. A pulley can also give a mechanical advantage. Both gears and pulleys reduce the effort required.

*Shaft of worm gear with screw thread*

*Toothed wheel of worm gear*

## LET'S EXPERIMENT
### CHANGING GEARS

**FIND OUT HOW CHANGING** gear makes a bike go slower or faster. **You will need**: an adult to help; bike with multiple gears (such as a mountain bike); gloves; coloured tape.

**1** A bike with multiple gears has different-sized chainwheels, to which the cranks and pedals are fixed, and different-sized sprockets (gears) on the rear wheel. Ask an adult to turn the bike upside-down and to hold the frame steady. Wear gloves to protect your fingers. Slowly, turn the pedals until one of the cranks is vertical. Mark a point on the rear tyre with coloured tape.

**Low gear**
*Rear tyre*
*Crank*
*Pedal*

**2** In low gear, the chain connects a small chainwheel and a large rear sprocket. Slowly, turn the crank once. Watch the tape mark. How many times does the rear wheel turn? How much force is needed to turn the pedals?

**3** In high gear, the chain connects a large chainwheel to a small sprocket. Turn the crank again. How many times does the rear wheel turn? How much force is needed on the pedals?

**4** In high gear, you need more force on the pedals, but the rear wheel turns faster. In low gear, you need less force and the wheel turns slower – helpful when riding your bike uphill!

**High gear**
*Chain*

*Rear sprocket hub*
*Chainwheels*   *The rear wheel powers the bicycle. The front wheel controls steering.*

*Bevel gear*

*Turning the handle of this egg whisk sets the bevel gear in motion, which turns the beater.*

## GEARING UP

On a bike, a chain connects the toothed gears on the chainwheel and rear wheel hub. In most gear systems, sets of gears mesh (link) directly with their teeth, so when one gear turns, the other turns with it. A worm gear (above) transmits motion at right angles as the toothed wheel meshes with the screw thread on the shaft. Bevel gears (left) have slanting teeth that also mesh at right angles. Gears with straight teeth that mesh together are called spur gears. They transmit motion between parallel toothed shafts, as in a car gearbox.

### Gear ratios

In machines, meshing gears usually change the speed of motion. A small gear with few teeth will drive a large one with many teeth more slowly. A gear with 12 teeth, for instance, must turn twice in order to turn a gear with 24 teeth once. Therefore, the gear ratio is two to one (2:1). Mechanical clocks and watches use a train of meshing gears with precise gear ratios to turn the hands at the correct speed for accurate time-keeping.

*A series, or train, of gears drives the hands of this watch.*

# PULLEYS AND CRANES

The simplest kind of pulley is a rope running over a grooved wheel. The wheel is fixed to a support with a load attached to one end of the rope. The load can be lifted by applying force, or pulling, the other end of the rope. While a single pulley doesn't give a mechanical advantage, it does make lifting easier by changing the direction of force required. Adding other pulleys increases the force applied, which means less effort is required – a mechanical advantage. A building crane gets much of its lifting power from a multiple pulley system called a block and tackle, which is positioned at the lifting end of the rope.

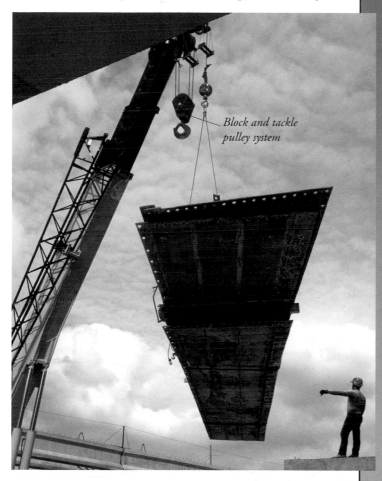

*Block and tackle pulley system*

## Brunelleschi's dome

The Italian architect Filippo Brunelleschi (1377–1446) is believed to have invented a crane called a swivelling jib for use in building the huge dome of this famous cathedral in Florence, Italy. It was one of "the many machines invented by his divine genius", as his epitaph in the cathedral says. Building on the cathedral began in 1296. The dome itself was built between 1420–1436.

## LET'S EXPERIMENT
## WEIGHTLIFTING

**FIND OUT HOW** a set of pulleys (a block and tackle) can help you to lift loads more easily. **You will need**: an adult to help you; two blocks of wood; nail or gimlet; two screw hooks; four screw eyelets (with closed metal rings); two lengths of strong string; candle; firm support (such as a rail attached to the wall); a load to be lifted (such as a bag of oranges).

**1** Ask an adult to make small starter holes in the two blocks of wood with a nail or gimlet – one hole in the middle of one side of each block and two holes evenly spaced in the opposite side. In each block, screw a hook into the single hole and screw two eyelets into the holes on the opposite side. Using a length of string, hang one block of wood from the support by its hook. Rub the other string with the edge of the candle. The wax will reduce the friction between the string and the pulleys.

**2** Thread the waxed string through the rings of the wooden blocks in a zigzag pattern to make the pulleys. Attach a load to the bottom hook, then pull on the free end of the string. You will find that you need less effort to lift the load with the pulley than if you picked it up directly. Try threading the string in different ways to compare the effort needed to lift the load.

*String attached to support*

*Pulleys*

*Waxed string*

*Secure the end of the string around the first ring.*

*Pulley*

*Pull this end of the string*

*Load*

# TIME AND MOTION

**WE'RE AWARE THAT TIME IS PASSING WHEN WE** see the hands of a clock going round, or when we look older each year. We tend to think of time flowing forwards at a steady pace, but the German physicist Albert Einstein (1879–1955) showed that the pace of time depends on how fast we're moving. Time is measured in seconds, minutes, hours, days, months, and years. A year is the length of time it takes the Earth to orbit once around the Sun, while a day is how long it takes the Earth to spin once on its axis. In order to co-ordinate time, the Earth is divided into 24 time zones by lines running from pole to pole, called lines of longitude. Time in each zone is measured from the 0° line of longitude that runs through Greenwich, UK.

*Digital watch*

# CLOCKS AND WATCHES

In order to keep time, clocks and watches are controlled by a mechanism with a constantly repeating motion. Early clocks used a swinging pendulum to keep time. Modern pendulum clocks may gain or lose up to 0.01 of a second in a day. Many smaller clocks and watches use a balance wheel that rocks to and fro at a steady rate. More accurate clocks are controlled by the vibrations of a quartz crystal. Quartz clocks are much more accurate than even the best pendulum clocks.

*There are 24 hours in a day.*

*There are 60 minutes in an hour.*

*There are 60 seconds in a minute.*

# ATOMIC CLOCKS

When scientists measure time they need to be very accurate. Ordinary clocks just won't do the job. Instead they use a special type of clock known as an atomic clock, which is kept regular by the vibrations of atoms or molecules. In fact, an atomic clock is so accurate that it is used to define the standard second. All atoms can absorb and emit electromagnetic radiation, and the standard second is measured by counting 9,192,631,770 vibrations of the radio waves that caesium atoms can absorb. This picture (left) shows the first caesium atomic clock. It was built at the UK's National Physical Laboratory in 1955.

11:00 | 12:00 | 13:00 | 14:00 | 15:00 | 16:00 | 17:00 | 18:00 | 19:00 | 20:00 | 21:00 | 22

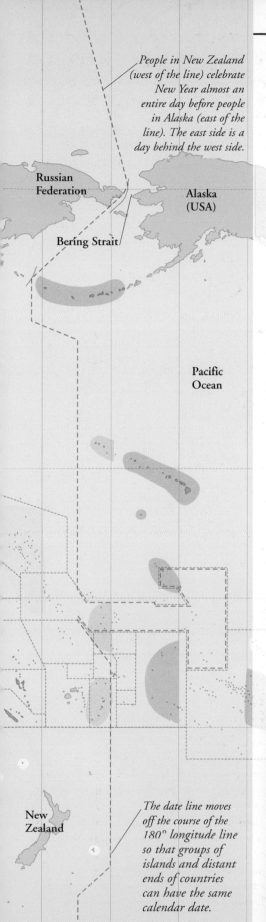

*People in New Zealand (west of the line) celebrate New Year almost an entire day before people in Alaska (east of the line). The east side is a day behind the west side.*

Russian Federation

Bering Strait

Alaska (USA)

Pacific Ocean

New Zealand

*The date line moves off the course of the 180° longitude line so that groups of islands and distant ends of countries can have the same calendar date.*

# DATE LINE

In time zones to the east of the Greenwich 0° line, time is ahead of Greenwich Mean Time (GMT). Zones west of Greenwich are behind GMT. Exactly half-way round the globe from Greenwich is the International Date Line (left). At 12 noon GMT, the day is ending on the west side of this line, and the same day is just beginning on the east side. There is a time difference of a day between either side.

## Time travel

According to Einstein, time travel into the future is possible. His Special Theory of Relativity, published in 1905, states that time speeds up or slows down depending on how fast you are travelling. If, for example, you went on a year-long trip around the Universe in a spaceship, travelling one per cent slower than the speed of light, time, for you, would slow down. In fact, it would go so slow that although your onboard clock would tell you that you've been travelling for one year, seven years will have passed for people on Earth. So when you return home, you will have travelled six years into the future. No-one knows whether time travel into the past is possible. But because time and space are linked, some scientists believe that travelling through wormholes (tunnels connecting two points in "spacetime") could lead to the past.

## Biological clock

Many of the processes of living organisms, such as people sleeping, animals migrating, and plants sprouting, happen at regular intervals. These intervals are timed by an internal "biological clock", which, in animals, is thought to be in the brain. We become aware of our biological clocks if we fly across several time zones. If you were to leave New York, USA, in the evening and fly to London, UK, you would arrive during the UK's morning. You would feel like sleeping in the day, and be awake during the night. The tiredness and other effects you feel as your biological clock adjusts to the new time zone are called jet lag.

## Star time

In solar time, one day equals the time it takes the Earth to spin once on its axis in relation to the Sun. Because the Earth is orbiting the Sun as well as spinning, the stars appear in a different place in the sky at the same time each night. To locate stars, astronomers use sidereal time (time relating to stars) rather than solar time. A sidereal day is how long it takes the Earth to rotate once in relation to a particular star. The rotation of the Earth is the reason the stars appear to move in circles, as this long-exposure photo shows.

3:00   00:00   01:00   02:00   03:00   04:00   05:00   06:00   07:00   08:00   09:00   10:00

# HEAT AND SOUND

**Picture:** *Shock waves form around a model plane when air reaches the speed of sound.*

# MOLECULES IN MOTION

**WHEN YOU LIE ON THE BEACH SUNBATHING,** listening to the waves crashing onto the shore, you are being bombarded with energy. The heat of the Sun and the sound of the waves are forms of energy that can be sensed; heat is felt and sound is heard. Both heat and sound involve the movement of molecules. Heat is the energy that moving molecules possess. It is often called internal energy and thermal energy. Sound is also a travelling vibration. It vibrates the molecules it travels through and can be picked up by our ears.

*Exploding firecrackers give out heat, light, and sound.*

## HEAT SOURCES

The Sun is the Earth's main source of heat. It makes our world a warm enough home for millions of different types of plants and animals. But we can only use a little of this heat directly, for example, in solar power schemes. We get most of the heat we use in our homes and industry by burning fuels, such as oil and natural gas. Fuels give off heat when they are burned. This heat may be converted into other forms of energy, such as electricity. In turn, the electricity can be turned back into heat again, in electric fires.

## HEAT ENGINES

The engines that power our cars, buses, ships, and planes all burn fuel and harness the fuel's heat. That is why we call them heat engines. Most of the fuels we use come from petroleum, or crude oil. Petroleum is converted to petrol for car engines, diesel for bus and ship engines, and kerosene for jet plane engines. Heat engines are not very efficient at harnessing the heat in their fuels. A petrol engine uses only about a quarter of the energy in its fuel. The rest is lost as heat in the exhaust gases, and friction among the moving parts.

## TEMPERATURE

We measure how hot something is by its temperature. But temperature is not the same as heat. Temperature measures the kinetic energy of molecules. Heat measures the total internal energy, kinetic and potential, of the entire substance. To understand the difference, compare a sparkler with a cup of hot tea. A spark from the sparkler has a much higher temperature than the cup of tea, but the tea has more heat over all. The spark's molecules are faster but fewer than in the cup of tea. So when all the molecular energies are added together to find the amount of heat, the tea has more heat because it has so many more molecules.

*This Cassini space probe contains a generator powered by thermoelectricity.*

*Sperm is preserved at very low temperatures.*

# MOVING

## HEAT

If you go outside without a coat on a cold day, heat escapes from your warm body into the cold air. Back inside, heat from a hot fire travels to your cold body to warm you up. Whenever heat moves, it always travels from a warmer object to a cooler one. This is a basic law of thermodynamics, the study of heat and energy movement. There are three ways in which heat can travel, or be transferred – conduction, convection, and radiation. In conduction and convection, molecules pass on the heat. In radiation, no medium is needed. It can take place in a vacuum.

*With their large ears, fennec foxes can pick up the faintest sounds.*

*Heat radiates from a red-hot horseshoe.*

## SOUND WAVES

One thing that can't travel through a vacuum is sound. Sound is carried by waves made by vibrating molecules. In a vacuum there are no molecules and therefore no sound. Our world is full of sound because it is surrounded by air. But the Moon is silent since it has no air. We tend to think about sound travelling only through air. But sound travels though any material. If you place a ticking clock on a table, then put your ear to the table, you'll hear the ticking loud and clear. The sound travels through the molecules in the table.

## EARS AND VOICES

People hear sounds when vibrations, travelling through the air or another material, reach their ears. Most animals pick up sounds in a similar way, with ears in their heads. But some animals are different. The cricket, for example, has ears on its legs; the mosquito picks up sounds with its antennae. Of course, sounds are not only heard, they are also made – with voices. Vibrations again hold the key to making sounds. When we speak, we make bands of tissue in our throat vibrate. These set up vibrations in the air as we breathe out.

*Voice patterns are made visible on an oscilloscope.*

## NOISE AND MUSIC

Our world is full of sound – of people talking, music playing, traffic hooting, and so on. High levels of sound can damage the ears. Some of these sounds are pleasant, others are considered unpleasant – they are noise. The difference between pleasant sounds, such as music, and noise often lies in the nature of the vibrations. Music is made up of regular vibrations at regular intervals, which the brain can sort out. Noise tends to be made up of irregular vibrations at irregular intervals, which the brain finds harder to cope with.

*Xylophone players make music by hammering.*

**1847** English physicist James Joule measures mechanical equivalence of heat.

**1877** American inventor Thomas Edison's phonograph makes the first sound recording.

**1895** German engineer Carl von Linde launches cryogenics.

**1911** Dutch physicist Kamerlingh Onnes finds superconductivity.

**1947** American Captain Charles (Chuck) Yeager breaks sound barrier in a Bell X-1 rocket plane.

**1997** Thrust SSC Supersonic car breaks sound barrier on land, reaching 1,228 kmh (763 mph).

# HEAT AND TEMPERATURE

**HEAT IS A FORM OF ENERGY – AND IT IS** all around us. Heat is found in the air, in the sea, in the rocks, in our bodies, and even in ice and snow. All these things possess heat, or internal energy, because their molecules are moving. However, in each of these substances, the molecules are moving at different speeds. They move faster in our bodies than they do in snow, for example, which means our bodies are warmer than snow. The temperature scale – a measure of heat energy – is used to tell us how hot or cold things are.

## HIDDEN HEAT

On hot days, we sweat a lot. Our bodies give off little beads of water, which evaporate into the air. To evaporate, water has to take in heat. So it takes in heat from our skin, which helps cool us. This heat is called latent heat. Latent heat is the heat taken in or given out when any substance changes its state. Most changes of state, such as melting and boiling, take place at a fixed temperature.

## ◄ EARTH HEAT ►

Deep inside the Earth, the rocks are hot. In volcanic regions, hot rocks are found near the surface. When water drains into a deep hole down among the hot rocks, it boils into steam. When the steam pressure is high enough, it forces water back up the hole and into the air as a geyser. In some areas, engineers are harnessing this geothermal ("Earth-heat") energy to produce electricity. **74** ►

*The geyser Pohutu ("Big Splash") erupts. It is the biggest geyser in New Zealand.*

## MEASURING TEMPERATURE

We measure temperature with a thermometer. Common thermometers work on the principle that liquids expand when the temperature rises. They consist of a liquid (usually mercury or coloured alcohol) in a narrow glass tube. When the temperature increases, the liquid expands and rises in the tube. Press-on strip thermometers use special liquid crystals that change colour as the temperature changes. In science, temperatures are usually measured in degrees on the Celsius scale. On this scale, water freezes at 0° and boils at 100°. Normal body temperature is 37°.

*Taking a child's temperature with a strip thermometer*

*Taking the temperature of a furnace with a pyrometer*

### Hot stuff

Ordinary thermometers are no use for measuring very high temperatures, such as those of furnaces or red-hot lava. Instruments called pyrometers ("fire-measurers") are used instead. A common type matches the colour of a glowing electric filament (wire) with the colour of the hot object. When the colours match, the temperatures are the same. The temperature of the filament is calculated from the current passing through it.

### FAHRENHEIT'S SCALE

The German physicist Daniel Gabriel Fahrenheit (1686–1736) made the first mercury thermometer in 1714, and devised the temperature scale named after him. On this scale, water freezes at 32° and boils at 212°. Normal body temperature is 98.6°.

°F
190
180
170
160
150
140
130
120

**YOU CAN MAKE A** simple thermometer using water, which will expand and contract as the temperature changes. Allow plenty of time for it to reach the temperature of its surroundings. **You will need:** small bottle; modelling clay; long, plastic tube (such as a drinking straw); ink; water; card; tape; pen; ruler; fridge; airing cupboard; a thermometer that ranges 0–50°C.

**1** Fill a bottle to the brim with water coloured with ink. Using modelling clay, make a stopper-shape to fit in the opening of the bottle. Push the plastic tubing through the clay, making sure it is airtight. Push the clay and the straw into the neck of the bottle, and the liquid will rise in the tube. Tape a piece of card to the tube for a scale.

*Setting up*

**2** Now you need to calibrate your thermometer to show temperature levels. Place it in a refrigerator with the other thermometer. After about half an hour, take out your thermometer. Mark on the scale where the water level comes to. Write next to it the temperature shown by the other thermometer.

*In the fridge*

**3** Now place your thermometer in an airing cupboard, again with the other thermometer. (If you don't have an airing cupboard, immerse the bottle and thermometer in a beaker of warm tap water.) After about half an hour, take out and mark where the water level comes to. Write down the temperature shown on the other thermometer.

*In the airing cupboard*

**4** You now need to complete your scale by dividing up the distance between the two points you have marked into equal parts. If your low temperature was 4°C and your high was 44°C, you will need to divide the distance between them into 40 parts. When you have done this, your thermometer will be ready to use.

*Calibrated*

# COLD SCIENCE

The Antarctic is the coldest place on Earth, where temperatures fall as low as -89°C. Scientists can produce even lower temperatures that can make gases turn to liquids and even freeze. The study of very low temperatures is called cryogenics. The lowest theoretical temperature that can be reached is absolute zero (-273.15°C), when all molecular motion ceases. It is the starting point for the Kelvin temperature scale, widely used in science. The units on this scale are called kelvins (K). Absolute zero is 0K, the freezing point of water just over 273K.

*A sample of human sperm, preserved in a tank of liquid nitrogen (about -196°C, 77K).*

**Super materials**
At temperatures of about 20K (-253°C) and below, some metals and alloys become superconductors, which can pass electricity without any resistance. At about 4K (-269°C), liquid helium becomes a superfluid and can flow without friction.

*Liquid helium cools instruments on infrared satellites.*

# HEAT ENERGY AND ENGINES

## WHEN WE LIGHT A FIRE TO KEEP WARM, THE

heat given out comes from a chemical reaction. This reaction is combustion (burning). When fuels burn, they combine chemically with the oxygen in the air, and as a result of this process, energy is given off as heat. We call this kind of reaction exothermic, which means "heat out". Some chemical reactions, however, take in heat and are called endothermic, which means "heat in". The heat from the combustion of fuels is the power source for all our common engines, which drive our cars, buses, ships, and planes. That is why we call them heat engines.

### James Joule
In the 1840s, the English physicist James Joule was one of the first to realize that heat is a form of energy. He therefore devised a system for measuring the heat produced by mechanical energy. The unit of energy, the joule (J), is named after him.

James Joule
(1818–89)

## CHEMICAL HEAT

When magnesium metal and copper oxide are heated together, they react, forming new chemicals and giving off even more heat (right). This additional heat is a result of a rearrangement of the chemical bonds between the reacting elements. Heating breaks the bonds between the elements in the original chemicals, and energy is absorbed. Then the elements form new bonds with one another to make new chemicals, and heat energy is given out. But the energy released in making new bonds is much greater than the energy absorbed in breaking the old ones, so overall energy is given out. The reaction is exothermic.

*The exothermic reaction of magnesium metal and copper oxide produces a white-hot flame.*

## SHOOTING STARS

When two objects are rubbed together, they become warm. The rubbing between the surfaces in contact (friction) generates heat. The faster you rub and the rougher the surfaces, the more heat is generated. When specks of rock from outer space fall into Earth's atmosphere, they are travelling at speeds of 60,000 kmh (40,000 mph) or more. Friction with the air molecules is so great that the specks become red-hot or white-hot and then burn up. We see the fiery trails these specks make in the night sky as meteors, popularly called shooting or falling stars.

# HEAT ENGINES

Just as mechanical energy can be converted into heat (as Joule proved), so heat can be converted into mechanical energy. We call the machines that do this heat engines. The first engines harnessed the heat energy of steam. The modern version of the steam engine is the steam turbine. It is classed as an external combustion engine because its fuel is burned outside the engine. In most other engines, such as petrol, diesel, and jet engines, fuel is burned inside, and they are classed as internal combustion engines.

*Induction – fuel mixture is taken in.*

*Intake valve*

*Compression – fuel mixture is compressed.*

*Spark plug*

*Exhaust – burned gases are forced out.*

*Piston*

*Exhaust valve*

*Power – fuel burns, driving down piston.*

## Burning inside
Petrol engines power most cars. The pistons in the cylinders produce power according to a regular cycle of four strokes (movements up or down). In each cylinder, a mixture of petrol and air is taken in, compressed, then set alight by an electric spark. The hot gases produced expand and push against the piston to produce power. Finally, the burned gases are removed and released through the exhaust.

## Burning outside
Steam turbines power this generator in a coal-fired power station. The heat from the burning coal turns water to steam in a boiler. The steam is fed into the turbines and expands through a series of turbine wheels, causing them to spin round and generate electricity.

---

**THIS BOAT HARNESSES** the energy of a burning candle. Heat from the flame turns the water in the coil into steam. The steam forces water out of the tubing and drives the boat forwards. Immediately, the steam cools, condenses, and shoots back up the tubing as water. This process sails the boat along in a series of pulses. **You will need:** an adult's help; soft plastic bottle; knife; 3 mm (¹/₈ in)-wide soft metal tubing; tubing cutter or hacksaw; sandpaper; pencil; nail, nightlight candle; adhesive tape; match; container of water.

## LET'S EXPERIMENT
### MAKING A STEAM BOAT

**1** Ask an adult to cut the bottle in half lengthways and to cut the metal tubing to about twice the length of the bottle. Sandpaper the ends of the tube. Gently bend the tubing around a pencil to make a coil. Using a nail, pierce two holes into the back end of the boat and push the tubing through to form a tight fit. Tape the candle to the bottom of the boat and gently bend the tubing so that the coil rests directly above the flame.

**2** Fill the tubing with water by placing one end in the water and carefully sucking at the other. Then place the boat on the surface of a large container of water, making sure the tube ends are both under the surface. Light the candle. After a few moments, the boat will begin to move along in a series of pulses. As long as the boat has a heat source and an engine full of water, it should continue to move.

*Your steam boat moves along in pulses.*

# EXPANSION AND CONTRACTION

**SOMETIMES THE LIDS ON JARS FIT SO** tightly that they're difficult to open. But if you put them under a hot tap, you'll find that they open more easily. This is because the heat from the water makes the lids expand (get bigger). Most things expand when they are heated. Adding more heat to a substance makes its molecules vibrate, or move about vigorously, and take up more room. On the other hand, when a substance cools, it contracts (gets smaller). Its molecules don't move as much and therefore take up less room. Almost all materials – solids, liquids, and gases – expand or contract when the temperature changes.

## EFFECTS ON SOLIDS

When engineers build a long bridge, they don't build it all in one piece. If they did, stresses (forces) occurring when the bridge expanded in hot weather would make it buckle or crack. Instead, the bridge is built in sections with gaps in between. These gaps allow the bridge to expand without causing any damage. For the same reason, concrete roads are laid in sections with expansion gaps in between. Solids don't expand as much as liquids and gases. Iron, for example, expands only by about 100,000th of its length for each one degree Celsius rise in temperature. Brass expands half as much again.

*A clinical thermometer*

**Thermostat**
The unequal expansion of metals can be used to work switches called thermostats. A thermostat controls the temperature in a room, for example, by switching an air conditioner on when the temperature rises above a certain level. It is worked by a bimetallic strip, made up of two metals joined together. When the temperature rises too high, one metal expands more than the other. This causes the strip to bend and make electrical contact, which switches on the air conditioner.

*Unequal expansion of metals makes strip bend.*

## MERCURY RISING

In liquids, the molecules are further apart than they are in solids. This means that they are not so strongly attracted to one another. So when you give them more energy (by heating), they can travel much faster and move even further apart. We make use of the expansion of liquids in thermometers. Mercury is a good liquid for thermometers because it is easy to see and expands (and contracts) evenly as the temperature changes. A clinical thermometer has a constriction in the bore to stop the mercury falling back after the temperature has been taken.

# EXPANSION

When explosives are detonated, they produce large amounts of gases and heat. The heated gases expand rapidly and cause a shock wave in the air that we hear as a bang. If a gas can't expand into a bigger volume when the temperature rises, then its pressure goes up. The volume, temperature, and pressure of a gas are related by three fundamental laws known as the gas laws (pp. 28–29). The expansion and contraction of gases explains how heat travels by convection.

### The Montgolfiers
Expanding air helped to pioneer early flight. In June 1783, the French brothers Jacques and Étienne Montgolfier built a big linen and paper bag with an opening at the base, and lit a fire beneath it. As the air inside heated up, it lifted the balloon into the air.

*An artist's imaginative impression of the first human flight on 21 November 1783.*

## LET'S EXPERIMENT
## GASES AND HEAT

**GASES EXPAND A LOT** when they're heated, and contract a lot when cooled. You can easily demonstrate this in a simple experiment.

**You will need:** a plastic bottle; a glass beaker or any other large container; a balloon; hot water from the hot tap (do not use boiling water); ice.

**1** At room temperature, stretch the neck of a balloon over the mouth of a bottle. The balloon will hang down limply. Now place the bottle in a large beaker of hot water. The limp balloon starts inflating and eventually stands upright as the air inside the bottle expands.

**2** Now place the bottle in a beaker of ice and water. The balloon immediately starts deflating, and may eventually be drawn into the neck of the bottle. This happens because the air in the bottle has cooled and contracted.

# TRAVELLING HEAT

**AFTER A FROSTY NIGHT, THE METAL LATCH ON A**
wooden gate feels much colder than the wood. Yet they both
have the same temperature. This happens because metal
conducts (passes) the heat away from your hand faster than
wood does. Conduction is one of the three main ways in
which heat travels. It happens in all materials – in solids,
liquids, and gases. Also all materials give off heat by radiation.
In liquids and gases, heat can also travel by convection.

*This metal frying
pan conducts the heat
from the hob to the food.*

## CONDUCTION

Solids are the best conductors. They are made up of
particles (atoms or molecules) held in a rigid framework.
They don't change places, but they do vibrate. When a
solid is heated in one place, the particles there gain more
energy and start vibrating more vigorously. They make
neighbouring particles vibrate more vigorously too.
These do the same to their neighbours, and so on
throughout the material. Metals conduct heat
particularly well because their loosely-held electrons
quickly pass on vibrations from atom to atom.

## INSULATION

Polar bears are warm-blooded mammals, yet they live in freezing
Arctic temperatures. They retain their body heat because of a thick
layer of fat under their skin, as well as a thick coat of fur. Fat and
fur are poor conductors of heat, or good insulators. Fur traps small
pockets of air, which is an excellent insulator. Wool, wood, and
plastic foam all trap air too, making them all suitable as insulators.

**Rotating radiometer**
A radiometer is a glass bulb
containing four vanes that
pivot around a vertical
support. The vanes are
painted black on one
side and silver on
the other. When left
in sunlight, the
vanes spin round.
The sunnier the day,
the faster the vanes
spin. The black sides
become hotter than the
silver, since black substances
absorb more solar radiation.
Air molecules meeting the
hotter black sides become
warmer, gain energy, and
accelerate away from them,
imparting a backwards force
(reaction) that spins the
vanes. So, the radiometer
spins with the silver sides
leading the spin.

*This vane
is painted
silver on the
side facing
us, and black
on its other,
hidden, side.*

**Beating the heat**
Insulating tiles made of silica cover most of the
space shuttle. They shield the craft and crew from
high temperatures. These temperatures are caused by
air friction when the shuttle plunges into Earth's
atmosphere after its journey into space.

*Thermal tiles
cover the space
shuttle orbiters.*

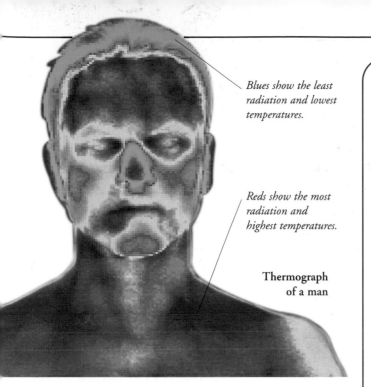

*Blues show the least radiation and lowest temperatures.*

*Reds show the most radiation and highest temperatures.*

**Thermograph of a man**

# RADIATION

Did you know that you are a radiator and give off heat like a radiator in a room? Using a technique called thermography, we can see the heat radiation that the body gives out. Every object radiates heat – the hotter it is, the more heat it radiates. Heat rays, or waves, belong to the same family of waves as light – electromagnetic waves (pp. 102–103). Heat waves are called infrared rays. Like all electromagnetic radiation, they can travel through space. That is how the Sun's heat reaches us.

## LET'S EXPERIMENT
### THE BEST RADIATORS

**THE AMOUNT OF HEAT A BODY** radiates depends not only on its temperature, but also on the nature of its surface. In this experiment, you'll find out whether a black or a shiny surface is the better radiator.

**You will need:** an adult's help; two jars with lids; matt black paint; paint brush; shiny kitchen foil; drill and bit; thermometer; water; modelling clay.

**1** Wrap shiny foil around one jar and paint the other matt black. Get an adult to drill a hole in each lid for the thermometer. Fill the jars with hot water from the tap, screw on their lids and take their temperatures. Place a piece of modelling clay over the lid holes to seal the jars.

**2** Every few minutes, take the temperature of each jar. Are they the same? You'll find that they aren't. The black jar cools down faster than the shiny one, because black bodies are the best radiators.

## LET'S EXPERIMENT
### CONVECTION IN WATER

**HEAT IS SPREAD BY CONVECTION** in all fluids – liquids as well as gases. In this experiment, you can see convection currents in action when water is heated.

**You will need:** an adult present; coloured paper; hole-punch; spoon; water; a heat source (such as a gas burner or a stove); heat-proof glass container (if using a stove, use a heat-proof glass bowl resting on a saucepan of water).

**1** Cut paper dots with a hole-punch. Stir them into a heat-proof container of water. Place the container over a heat source and gently heat it on one side.

**2** View the container from the side. Notice the dots begin to move as the water heats up. The ones directly over the heat source move upwards with the rising warmer, lighter (less dense) water. On the other side, the dots move down with the colder, denser water.

# CONVECTION CURRENTS

Hang-glider pilots launch themselves off cliffs, riding the warm air currents, which are called thermals, sweeping up from below. The upward currents are created when hot land heats the air above it. The air expands and becomes lighter (less dense) than the air around it, and therefore rises. At the same time colder, denser air descends to take its place. These circulating streams of rising and descending air are convection currents. On a large scale, convection currents cause the winds. On a small scale, they spread heat from radiators around a room.

# SOUND VIBRATIONS

**IF YOU TOUCH YOUR BICYCLE BELL WHEN IT IS RINGING,** you feel it vibrating, or moving rapidly to and fro. It is these vibrations that produce the ringing sound you hear. As the bell vibrates outwards, it pushes against the air molecules next to it and sets them vibrating too. In turn, these molecules set the next ones vibrating, and the vibrations, or waves, spread through the air away from the bell. We hear these vibrations as sound when they reach our ears. In fact, every sound you hear is created by something vibrating. Sometimes you can see the vibration; sometimes you cannot.

## VIBRATIONS IN THE AIR

A hummingbird beats its wings as fast as 70 times a second as it hovers in front of a flower. The rapid beating of its wings creates vibrations in the air, which produce the humming noise that gives the birds their name. It is also the rapid beating of wings that creates the buzzing sound made by bees and other flying insects. Male grasshoppers produce their distinctive sound by rubbing together parts at the base of their wings, called the file and scraper.

*Compression*          *Rarefaction*          *Compression*

### Sound waves

Sound waves travel through materials in much the same way as waves travel through a "slinky" spring (above). When a sound is made, the air molecules near the sound are squashed together and create a high-pressure area called a compression. They, in turn, jostle up to the molecules next to them and then are pulled back into place. This action creates a low-pressure area called a rarefaction. Sound waves are longitudinal. This means that they vibrate in the direction in which they are travelling.

*Cochlea*          *Ear bones*

*Eardrum*          *Opening of the ear canal*

**Hear this**
The ear canal funnels sound waves to the eardrum. The eardrum vibrates and then three ear bones carry the vibrations to the hearing organ, the cochlea. The cochlea contains fluid, so sound waves travel through it easily. It is also lined with hairs that detect the vibrations and send sound signals to the brain.

## LOUDNESS

The ground staff at airports who guide aircraft into parking bays wear ear defenders. This is to protect their ears against the loud noise of jet engines. Loudness is the term we generally use for the intensity (amount of energy) the sound waves carry. Big vibrations have a lot of energy and produce intense sound waves with a large amplitude – the distance the air molecules vibrate back and forth. Therefore, the further the molecules move, the greater is the intensity, or loudness of the sound.

130 dB

100 dB

80 dB

40 dB

20 dB

### The decibel scale

We measure sound intensity (loudness) on the decibel (dB) scale. One decibel is one-tenth of a bel, a unit named after Alexander Graham Bell, who invented the telephone. The quietest sound we can hear is 0 dB, while the sound of a jet plane taking off is an ear-splitting 130 dB. But this figure does not mean that the aircraft is 130 times louder than the quietest sound. The decibel scale is logarithmic, which means that an increase of 10 dB increases loudness ten times. In other words, a sound of 130 dB sounds ten times as loud as one of 120 dB.

**WE CANNOT SEE** sound waves in the air, but we can sometimes see the effects of the vibrations. This experiment clearly shows that sound is simply vibration.
**You will need:** tuning fork; a glass; water.

**1** Fill the glass to the brim with water. Strike the tuning fork sharply (preferably on a wooden surface) so that it produces a note.

**2** Now touch the surface of the water with the prongs of the tuning fork. The water will immediately splash out, driven by the vibrations of the fork.

# ECHOES AND ACOUSTICS

If you shout when you are in a large, empty building, you can often hear the sound of your voice coming back to you as an echo. Echoes are sounds that have been reflected (bounced) off surfaces around you. Hard surfaces reflect sound more effectively than soft surfaces. Soft surfaces tend to absorb sound. The way the design of a building affects sound is called its acoustics. Concert halls and theatres must be carefully designed so that echoes do not interfere with the sounds of speech or music reaching the audience. The Greeks and Romans built amphitheatres (below) with superb acoustics.

*Large ears give bats more sensitive hearing.*

### Locating by echoes

Echoes play a vital role in the lives of most bats. Bats fly at night when ordinary eyes are no good for finding the way, so they use their ears instead. They send out high-pitched sound signals that echo from any object in their path. The bat picks up the signals again and builds a picture of sounds that enables it to navigate its way through the darkness. This technique is known as echolocation.

# SPEED AND FREQUENCY

**COMPARED WITH LIGHT, SOUND TRAVELS**
relatively slowly. When you see someone
hammering in the distance, you hear the sound
after you see the hammer strike. Under the
same conditions, all sound waves travel at the
same speed. But they can vibrate in different
ways. Some vibrate quickly – they have a high
frequency or pitch (like the voice of a soprano).
Others vibrate slowly – they have a low
frequency (like the voice of a bass). We measure
frequency in hertz (Hz), the number of waves
passing a point each second. Humans can hear
sounds between about 20 and 20,000 Hz.

## WHALE SONG

Sound travels more than four times faster in water than in air
and is carried for long distances. The molecules in water are
more densely packed and pass on the vibrations more easily.
Whales can, therefore, communicate with each other by sound
over distances of 30 km (20 miles) or more. Male humpback
whales are noted for their "singing" during the mating season.
Their songs are complex symphonies of repeated melodies and
phrases and may last for a day or more. The whales sing either
to attract a mate or to warn off other males.

*A cloud forms behind the
plane as it breaks the
sound barrier.*

## THE SOUND BARRIER

At sea level, sound travels through the air at a
speed of around 1,225 kmh (760 mph). This is
called sonic speed. When a plane travels at below
sonic speed, sound waves travel in front of it. But
when it reaches sonic speed, the sound waves pile
up on the plane to create a shock wave. When
the plane goes supersonic (flying faster than
sound), it leaves a shock wave behind, which is
heard on the ground as a loud bang called a sonic
boom. It was once thought that the shock wave
set off at sonic speed would shatter a plane and
was a barrier, or obstacle, to supersonic flight.
This came to be known as the sound barrier.

# ULTRASONICS

Humans cannot hear sound waves with frequencies over about 20,000 Hz. These are called ultrasonic waves. We may not be able to hear them, but we can make use of them. Pregnant women have ultrasound scans to check on the health of their unborn babies. A scanner transmits ultrasonic waves into the womb, where they are reflected by the baby's body. The reflections are picked up and displayed on a screen (left). Ultrasonic waves are also used in sonar, a kind of sound radar that ships and submarines use in navigation. It works in the same way as echolocation in bats (p. 95).

*Waves stretch out as the ambulance travels past, producing a lower frequency.*

*Waves crowd together as the ambulance approaches, producing a higher frequency.*

**The Doppler effect**
When an ambulance races first towards, then away from you, you hear the sound of its siren change pitch, or frequency. This is called the Doppler effect. When the ambulance comes towards you, you hear more waves than usual per second (higher frequency). When the ambulance goes away, the sound waves are stretched out and you hear fewer waves than usual per second (lower frequency).

## ANIMAL HEARING

Some animals hear a different range of sound frequencies to humans. Snakes, for example, can hear only a narrow range of frequencies, from about 200 to 800 Hz. Bats, on the other hand, can hear frequencies from about 1,000 Hz to over 120,000 Hz. They use ultrasound for echolocation. Mice and moths hear ultrasounds too. Other animals can hear sounds with lower frequencies than we can hear. We call sounds at these frequencies infrasounds. Pigeons can hear sounds with frequencies as low as 0.1 to 10 Hz. This means they may have the ability to detect earthquake waves.

## LET'S EXPERIMENT
### BOUNCING SOUND

**SOUND WAVES ARE REFLECTED** from surfaces in much the same way as light waves. This is what causes echoes. In this experiment, find out which surfaces reflect sound best – soft or hard. **You will need:** two poster tubes; card; ticking watch (or clock); pieces of foam and fabric.

**1** Set up the card and tubes as shown in the picture. Leave a gap of about 6 cm (2.5 inches) between the ends of the tubes and the card. Place the watch at the mouth of one tube, and put your ear to the mouth of the other.

**2** You will be able to hear the watch ticking clearly. The sound has travelled along one tube and been reflected by the card into the other. Cover the card first with cloth, then with foam. Do they reflect the sound better or worse than before?

*Sound travels down the tube and bounces off the card.*

# MAKING MUSIC

**MUSICAL INSTRUMENTS CREATE SOUNDS** by making something vibrate. For example, guitars use vibrating strings. Most musical instruments are "tuned" to produce a set of frequencies, or notes. But the same note sounds different on different instruments. This is because each instrument produces its own distinctive range of vibrations, called harmonics, in addition to a basic vibration. The pattern of sound waves from a musical instrument can be represented as wavy lines, with peaks and troughs showing the change in air pressure as the sound reaches your ear.

Gong

### Percussion instruments
The gong is a percussion instrument, which you hit with a hammer. The sound waves have an irregular pattern, which we hear as a crashing noise. Other percussion instruments include the drum, triangle, and xylophone.

Flute

### Wind instruments
The flute is a wind instrument. Players blow over a hole to vibrate the air inside. It produces quite a pure sound, with a clean wave form. With other wind instruments, such as the oboe and clarinet, players blow through a reed to make the air vibrate.

*The sound waves shown for the flute (above) and the violin (below) are created when each instrument hits the same note. However, they each have their own distinctive wave pattern.*

## ALL TOGETHER NOW
A gamelan orchestra (above) in Southeast Asia plays traditional music with a distinctive sound. The performers play mainly percussion instruments such as gongs, chimes, and gamelangs, which are rather like xylophones. In Western countries, orchestras use a range of instruments, divided into four main types: strings, wind, brass, and percussion. Usually, a conductor keeps the musicians playing in time with each other. The conductor also determines the tempo (speed) of the music.

Violin

### Stringed instruments
The violin is a stringed instrument. The strings are made to vibrate with a bow. They produce a complex, "bright" sound with many harmonics. Other bowed stringed instruments include the viola and double bass. The guitar and harp are stringed instruments that are plucked to create sounds.

## LET'S EXPERIMENT
### MUSICAL BOTTLES

**WIND INSTRUMENTS WORK** by vibrating a column of air. You can make you own wind instrument from a row of bottles. **You will need:** eight identical bottles; water; food colouring (optional).

**1** Arrange bottles in a row and fill them with decreasing amounts of coloured water. Blow over the mouth of the bottles to make sounds.

**2** "Tune" each bottle by adjusting the water level so that it gives you a different note. Now you can play music!

**Synthesizing sound**
Most modern bands include a synthesizer among their instruments. This is so called because it synthesizes sounds, or makes sounds artificially by means of electronic circuits. Operated with a keyboard, synthesizers can reproduce the sound of all acoustic (non-electric) instruments. They can also produce special effects and unique sounds of their own.

# RECORDING SOUND

At a recording studio, singers sing into a microphone in time with a pre-recorded backing group which they hear through their headphones. Thomas Edison made the first ever sound recording in 1877, of the words "Mary had a little lamb". He used a needle attached to a vibrating disc moved by sound waves to scratch a groove in tinfoil. This groove method is the basis of recording on vinyl discs. Technological developments allowed sound to be recorded onto magnetic tape, while the more recent digitization process led to sound being stored on CDs (compact discs) and as digital audio files on computers and MP3 devices.

**Mixing sounds**
In a recording studio, the sounds of different instruments and voices are often recorded at different times. Sound engineers then take over to produce the finished recording. They use a device called a mixer to bring all the sounds together. Using the sliders on the mixing console (above), the sound engineer adjusts the loudness and tone of each individual performance to make a perfect blend.

*A CD carries sounds as numbers in a spiral track of pits.*

**Digital recording**
In modern digital recording, the wave forms of sounds are converted into precise numbers, which are then recorded in binary code (using just the numbers 0 and 1). On a CD, these numbers are recorded as pits and "lands" (flat areas), which are read by a laser to play the CD. In most digital audio files, the binary-coded files are shrunk down to about one-twelfth of their original size. These compressed files can then be stored and played on an MP3 player or other digital audio device.

*A digital audio device can be used to store and play music.*

# LIGHT AND COLOUR

**Picture:** *Rainbows form when sunlight passes through raindrops. Double bows are sometimes seen when the Sun is bright.*

# VISIBLE WAVES

## LIFE ON EARTH COULD NOT EXIST WITHOUT LIGHT.

It enables plants to grow and animals to survive. Light is a form of energy that we can think of as travelling in waves. It forms the small visible part of the electromagnetic spectrum, which also includes radio and television waves, microwaves, infrared (heat), ultraviolet (UV), X-rays, and gamma rays. Things that do not produce their own light are visible because light from another source is reflected off them. The Sun produces most of the natural light on Earth, while electric lighting is a common source of artificial light.

*The visible part of the electromagnetic spectrum*

## NATURAL LIGHT

On Earth, the main source of natural light is the Sun. Nuclear reactions at the core of the Sun create energy in the form of light (and heat). A few organisms, such as fireflies and glow-worms, produce natural light in their bodies through a chemical reaction called bioluminescence. For centuries, scientists debated whether light travelled as waves or as particles. In the early 20th century, research by German physicists Max Planck (1858–1947) and Albert Einstein (1879–1955) led to the current theory. Scientists now believe that light can travel both as waves and as tiny particles of energy called photons, but never both at the same time.

## INTERFERENCE

When two beams of light meet, they interfere with each other (p. 118). If the peaks of one light wave line up with the peaks of the other, constructive interference occurs and the waves add together to produce a brighter beam. However, if the peaks of one wave line up with the troughs of the other, destructive interference takes place and the beams cancel each other out. This combination results in a pattern of dark and light known as an interference pattern. These patterns can be obtained by shining light through a small glass slide engraved with thousands of narrow lines called a diffraction grating. As the light passes between the lines, it is split up into tiny beams that spread out and interfere with each other.

## LASERS

A laser produces a highly concentrated beam of light that can be strong enough to cut through metal. Most lasers have either gas, or a crystal such as a ruby, trapped inside a small space with mirrors at each end. A burst of very bright light or electricity causes the gas or crystal to produce light. The colour of this light depends on the substance trapped – rubies give red light, for example. This light reflects to and fro off the mirrors in the cavity. Each time the light passes through the crystal or gas, it

*Interference creates streaks of colours from the white light passing through this diffraction grating.*

*Picture of the Sun taken by the SOHO probe.*

When electricity passes through the mercury gas, it gives out ultraviolet light. Because we cannot see ultraviolet light, the insides of the tube are coated with fluorescent crystals which convert the ultraviolet light into visible light. Fluorescence also occurs in nature, for example, a fluorescent rock will glow under an ultraviolet lamp.

## LIGHT YEARS

Most stars are an extremely long way from the Earth. Kilometres or miles are not practical ways of measuring such enormous distances. For instance, one of the stars in the constellation Cygnus is approximately 100 million million kilometres (60 million million miles) away from Earth. Astronomers need a larger unit of measurement to describe distances in space, so they use light years. A light year is the distance that light travels in one year. Light from our next nearest star, Proxima Centauri, (the Sun is our nearest star) takes 4.3 years to reach us here on Earth, so it is 4.3 light years away.

*The red beam from this helium-neon laser is used to perform laser eye surgery.*

The electric field is the part of the light wave that interacts with matter. Normally, the electric field vibrates in many different directions, but if it is restricted to only one direction, the light is said to be polarized. Sunlight reflecting from a road tends to be horizontally polarized. Therefore, wearing sunglasses with polarizing filters that only let through vertically polarized light will block the glare.

## FLUORESCENCE

When neon gas is sealed in a glass tube and electricity is passed through it, the neon glows red. Often used in signs, neon lights based on this principle were the forerunners of fluorescent lights. Instead of using neon gas, fluorescent lights use mercury gas inside a glass tube.

causes them to give off even more light. Finally, an extremely powerful laser beam emerges from a small hole in one of the mirrors. Lasers have many uses, from medical surgery, to creating holograms, to reading the data on compact discs.

## POLARIZED LIGHT

Electromagnetic waves such as light waves have two parts, an electric field and a magnetic field. The two fields travel at right angles to the direction of the wave.

*Polarized light interference produces coloured stress patterns on this plastic hook.*

# LIGHT AND SHADE

**TRANSPARENT SUBSTANCES, SUCH AS GLASS,** let light through, but opaque materials, such as wood, block light. Light travels in straight lines, if it falls on an opaque object, a dark shadow is cast in the shape of the object where the light could not pass through. Every night we are plunged into shadow by the Earth. As it rotates, each place on the surface becomes shielded from the Sun's light for a few hours by the rest of the Earth. Shadows also fall over parts of the Earth's surface during solar eclipses.

Gnomon

### The shadows of time

Shadows can be used to tell the time. A sundial marks the time of day by the shadow cast on its surface as the Sun moves gradually across the sky. The object on a sundial that is used to create the shadow is called a gnomon. On this sundial (left), the shadow falls on a large metal ring raised at an angle to the ground. The ring has the hours of the day marked on it and the position on which the shadow of the gnomon falls tells the time.

Star's perceived position

Observer sees virtual image of hidden star

Sun

True position of star

## ‹ GENERAL RELATIVITY ›

The German-born theoretical physicist Albert Einstein (1879–1955) wrote two theories of relativity. His "general" theory of relativity published in 1916 describes gravity. It suggests that the force of gravity can bend light, so the gravity of planets and stars makes them act like giant lenses. British astrophysicist Arthur Eddington tested this theory during the solar eclipse of 1919. Eddington photographed stars whose light passed near to the Sun during the eclipse and compared them with photographs of the same stars taken when the Sun was in another part of the sky. The stars appeared to have moved slightly, proving that the Sun's gravity was indeed bending the light from them just as Einstein had predicted. This result made Einstein famous. 137▶

**Albert Einstein**

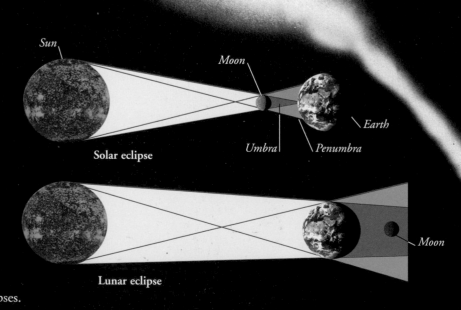

The diamond ring effect during a solar eclipse

## ULTIMATE SHADOW

A solar eclipse occurs when the Moon blocks out the Sun's light and casts a shadow on the Earth. Since the Moon does not completely obscure the Sun, a blurred shadow is produced. The dark middle of the blurred shadow is called the umbra, and the lighter shadow round the edges is the penumbra. During a solar eclipse, people in the umbra see a total eclipse, while those in the penumbra see a partial eclipse. Lunar eclipses occur when the Moon moves through the Earth's shadow. During a lunar eclipse, the Moon usually becomes red rather than completely dark. This colour comes from small amounts of sunlight refracted (pp. 108–09) by the Earth's atmosphere that still reach the Moon. Other planets, moons, and stars also produce eclipses.

Sun

Moon

Earth

Umbra

Penumbra

**Solar eclipse**

Moon

**Lunar eclipse**

*Each star eclipses the other during its orbit.*

Star

Centre of gravity

# BINARY STARS

Many of the stars we see are in fact binary stars. These are pairs of stars attracted to each other by gravity that orbit around each other. Some binaries are a type of variable star called an eclipsing binary. Their position in the sky means that when we look at them from Earth, each star repeatedly passes in front of the other blocking out its light. Astronomers identify eclipsing binaries from these changes in brightness. This nebula (right) photographed by the Hubble Space Telescope has a binary star at its centre.

Total solar eclipses 1998–2020

### Forecasting an eclipse

A solar eclipse occurs when a "new" Moon passes between the Earth and the Sun, and casts a shadow on the Earth's surface. There is a new Moon every 29.5 days, but solar eclipses only occur about every 18 months. This is because the path of the Moon's orbit around the Earth is tilted at an angle of five degrees compared to the path the Earth takes as it orbits around the Sun. Most of the time therefore the new Moon's shadow passes above or below the Earth. When viewing a solar eclipse, never look at the Sun without eye protection.

The corona at total eclipse of the Sun

**MAKE FUN SHADOWS** with shadow puppets. You will need: pencil; card; scissors; tape; torch.

**1** Draw the outline of a character onto the card. (You may want to copy these ghosts.) Carefully cut out the character and tape it to the end of the pencil.

**2** Hold the puppet near a wall, then shine the torch on it to make the shadow appear. Alternatively, hold your hands in front of the light and see what patterns you can make on the wall. Try clasping your hands and moving one or more of your fingers. Also note the effect of moving the torch to different positions.

### History of shadow

Shadow theatres are traditional in parts of Asia. In the 17th century, they spread to Europe, becoming the forerunners of modern movies. The rods attached to these Javanese puppets allow their jointed limbs to be moved.

# LET'S EXPERIMENT
## SHADOW PUPPETS

# REFLECTION

## MOST OBJECTS DO NOT

produce their own light. We only
see them because light is reflected
off them. That is why we cannot
see in the dark. Rough and
dark objects reflect less light than
lighter, shinier things. Mirrors reflect
back almost all of the light falling on
them. They can form images of objects
because unlike rough surfaces, which
scatter reflected light in many directions,
they reflect light rays in one direction and
in the same pattern in which they arrive.

*Torch with
red filter*

*Card with
vertical slit*

*Reflected
green ray*

*Protractor
on paper*

*Incident
red ray*

*Angle of
incidence*

*"Normal" line at
right angles (90º)
to the surface of
the mirror.*

*Angle of
reflection*

*Reflected
red ray*

*Top of
mirror*

*Base of mirror
against edge
of protractor*

*Incident
green ray*

## LAWS OF REFLECTION

There are always two rays involved in reflection – an
incident (incoming) ray and a reflected (outgoing) ray.
The angle between the incident ray striking any mirror
and an imaginary line called the "normal" that hits the

*Incident ray*

mirror at right angles is always
the same as the angle between
the "normal" and the reflected
ray. Both the rays and the
"normal" lie on the same
imaginary flat surface.
Images formed by flat mirrors
are virtual (appearing to be
behind the mirror) and
the wrong way round.

*Virtual
image*

*Reflected
ray*

*Flat
mirror*

## LET'S EXPERIMENT
### THE LAWS OF REFLECTION

**PROVE THAT THE ANGLE** of incidence of light on a mirror equals the
angle of reflection. **You will need:** two torches; coloured filters (such
as sweet wrappers); two pieces of card; scissors; large sheet of paper;
protractor; small mirror; modelling clay, pen.

**1** Fix a different
colour filter over
each torch. Cut a
vertical slit in each
card. Put the torches
on the floor. Place a
card in front of each,
so a narrow coloured
light shines through
the slit and onto the
mirror (see Step 2).

**2** Put the protractor
on the paper on
the floor. Supporting
the mirror with clay,
stand it against the
straight edge of the
protractor. On the
paper, mark the 90º
line, and the incident
ray and reflected ray
for each colour.

**3** For each colour,
the angle between
the 90º mark and the
incident ray should
equal the angle
between 90º and the
reflected ray. Move
the torches to other
positions. The two
angles will always
be equal.

*Torch with
green filter*

# OPTICAL FIBRES

Most of our telephone calls and e-mails are converted by electronics into pulses of light and carried by optical fibre cables to their destination. On arrival, more electronics turns the light back into sound or data. Optical fibres like the one on the right (pictured with a needle to show its size) are made from a very thin core of glass that can refract (bend) light strongly. This core is surrounded by a coating of glass, known as the cladding, that cannot bend light as much. If light enters the fibre at certain angles, the boundary between the core and the cladding acts like a mirror and reflects it to and fro down the fibre. Light pulses can travel long distances in this way.

### Endoscope
Bundles of optical fibres inside endoscopes (long, thin, medical instruments for seeing inside the body) transmit detailed images to television screens or an eyepiece for doctors to see. The area being studied is illuminated by light delivered by another bundle of fibres. Here surgeons are using an endoscope during keyhole surgery to remove a gallbladder.

### Reflecting telescope
A large concave mirror, called the primary mirror, collects the light from stars and planets inside reflecting telescopes. The light reflected off this mirror falls onto a smaller flat mirror and an image is created. The image can either be recorded on photographic film or viewed through the lenses in an eyepiece that magnify it. There are different shapes and arrangements of mirrors in reflecting telescopes. This version (right) was designed by Sir Isaac Newton (1642–1727). The world's largest telescope mirror (left), belonging to the Hobby-Eberly telescope at the McDonald Observatory in Texas, USA, is 11 m (36 ft) wide.

The Hobby-Eberly telescope mirror has 91 segments.

Light enters the telescope.

Eyepiece lenses

Flat mirror

Concave mirror collects the light

## CONCAVE AND CONVEX

Curved surfaces can either be concave, which means that they curve inwards, or convex, which means that they curve outwards. The mirrors we use to see our reflections are flat because although the images they produce are reversed from right to left, they are the same size and shape as the object. Curved mirrors produce distorted images that can be larger or smaller than the object reflected.

### Convex mirror
Rays of light reflected from convex mirrors spread out (diverge), which makes them appear to have come from a focal point behind the mirror. The virtual image formed behind the mirror is smaller than the object, so convex mirrors are used as rear-view mirrors in cars to help drivers see as much of the road behind as possible.

### Concave mirror
Light reflected from concave mirrors is focused in front of them. Depending on how close the object is, either a magnified, same size, or smaller real image (which lies in front of the mirror) or a magnified virtual image (which lies behind the mirror) is formed. Magnifying make-up and shaving mirrors are concave.

Astronauts' visors behave like convex mirrors.

Rays of light

Virtual focus

Mirror

Real focus

# REFRACTION

**WHEN LIGHT TRAVELS FROM ONE TRANSPARENT** substance into another, it changes direction slightly. This bending of light is known as refraction. If you look down at your legs while standing in water, they will appear bent. This is because light refracts as it passes from water to air. Curved pieces of transparent material that can refract light in a particular way are known as lenses. Most optical instruments, including binoculars, telescopes, and cameras, have lenses that focus light and produce an image of whatever is being viewed.

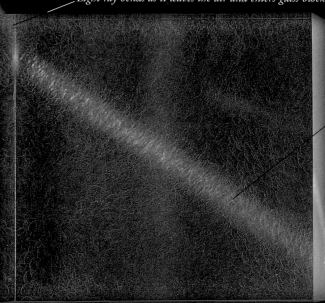

Light ray bends as it leaves the air and enters glass block.

Light inside the block travels in a straight line.

Light ray bends again as it leaves glass block and enters the air.

*Convex objective lens*

*Focal point*

*Light enters the telescope and is converged by the convex lens*

*Light rays*

*Concave eyepiece lens*

### The refracting telescope
Lenses inside refracting telescopes are used to produce magnified images of distant objects such as planets and stars. The large lens at the far end of the telescope collects light from the object and creates an image of it. The smaller lens at the near end is the eyepiece lens, which magnifies the image.

## LAWS OF REFRACTION
The picture on the left shows a ray of light bending as it moves from air into the top of a glass block, and bending again as it leaves the block at the bottom. In 1621, the Dutch mathematician Willebrord Snell (1580–1626) discovered that there is a precise mathematical relationship between the angle at which a light ray enters a substance that refracts it, and the angle it is refracted to. This relationship produces a number known as the refractive index that tells us how strongly a substance refracts light.

**Willebrord Snell**

## LENSES
Transparent materials such as glass and plastic are used to make lenses. Lenses refract light. Convex lenses cause light rays to converge (come together). The light focuses where the converging rays meet. Convex lenses make objects look larger or smaller, depending on their distance from the lens. Concave lenses cause light rays to diverge (spread out) and appear to come from a virtual focus the same side of the lens as the light enters. Concave lenses make objects look smaller.

**Convex lens**

*Direction of light rays*

**Concave lens**

### Short sight
For the human eye to see clearly, light rays coming into the eye should focus on the retina. A short-sighted person can see close objects clearly, but distant objects are blurred. This is because their eyes are too long, so light rays focus before reaching the retina, rather than on it. Spectacles with concave lenses correct the problem.

### Long sight
Distant objects look clear to a long-sighted person, but closer objects look blurred. Their eyes are too short, so light rays from close by focus behind the retina, rather than on it. A young person's natural lens can correct for this, otherwise spectacles with convex lenses are used.

*Eye of short-sighted person*

*Light rays from a distance*

*Lens*

*Concave lens*

*Light rays focus in front of retina*

*Retina*

*Light rays focus on retina*

*Eye of long-sighted person*

*Light rays from close by*

*Convex lens*

*Light rays focus behind retina*

*Light rays focus on retina*

*Cardboard roof prevents light escaping from the top of the box.*

**SEE HOW LIGHT** is refracted when it passes through transparent objects. **You will need:** cardboard box; scissors; small lamp; white card; transparent jars, bottles, and lenses.

**1** Remove the top and bottom of the box and cut narrow slits in each of its sides. Experiment by cutting a different number of slits in each side, for example, cut seven close together on one side and three spaced out on another.

*A water-filled jam jar makes a great convex lens*

*Focal point*

*Fill a small bottle with water and stand it in the path of the light rays. The bottle acts as a convex lens, refracting and converging the rays. The rays of light meet at a place called the focal point.*

**2** Put the lamp on a sheet of white card and place the box on top of it. Make a roof with card so that light does not escape through the top of the box.

**3** Darken the room, then place the transparent objects in the path of the light rays coming from the box. See how these objects act as convex lenses, bringing the rays to a focal point. Try a concave lens as well (see below).

*Position a convex lens in front of the light rays. The more curved a lens is, the closer it will focus the light. So the bottle (above) focuses the light nearer than the lens.*

*Concave lens*

*Concave lens bends light outwards.*

**Concave lens**
Place a concave lens in one of the light ray paths. See how the light diverges as it does in this picture (left).

*Focal point*

*Fresnel lighthouse lens*

**Cataract surgery**
Old age and certain diseases can cause an opaque area – through which light cannot pass – called a cataract to form on the normally transparent lens of the eye. Cataracts cause blurred vision or blindness. To correct this, the affected lens is removed in an operation and replaced by a plastic lens.

# LIGHTHOUSE

Ships can be warned of potential danger, and find where they are, by the light from a lighthouse like this one in South Africa. French physicist Augustin Fresnel (1788-1827) designed a lighthouse lens like this one in the 1820s. The lens gives a strong beam of light, and versions of it are used today to project beams visible for 28 miles. The first lighthouse was built around 280 BC, and guided ships into the harbour at Alexandria in Egypt.

# OPTICAL ILLUSIONS

**MOST OF THE TIME OUR BRAINS INTERPRET THE** signals coming from our eyes correctly. But occasionally we're tricked into thinking we see something that isn't really there. We call this an optical illusion. Some optical illusions, such as mirages, occur naturally. Others, such as the illusion of depth on a flat surface, or pictures with impossible shapes, are artificially created for fun. The way we interpret information from our senses is called perception. Past experience of sensing things is a factor that can shape perception.

*Our brains interpret this tribar as an impossible 3D shape.*

# MIRAGES

If a layer of warm air forms near the ground beneath a cooler layer of air, an effect known as an oasis mirage may occur. Light rays from distant objects are refracted (bent) as they pass from cool air into warmer air. The light rays bend upwards to our eyes and appear to be coming from the ground. We therefore see an upside-down image of the object – as in this mirage (above) photographed in the Western Desert in

Egypt. It appears to be in a pool of water, which is in fact an image of the blue sky. No wonder mirages have driven many thirsty travellers to despair!

*Cold air*
*Straight light ray*
*Hot air*
*Refracted ray*
*Virtual image*

# PERSPECTIVE

In real life, objects appear more blurred, and paler and bluer in colour, the further into the distance they are. Artists mimic this effect when painting landscapes to give a three-dimensional (3-D) illusion on a two-dimensional (2-D) canvas. This technique is called atmospheric perspective. When looking into the distance, we also see any parallel lines – such as the sides of a long, straight road – converge. They appear to meet at an imaginary "vanishing point". Artists use this optical illusion, known as linear perspective, as another way of givinga picture depth. Objects are drawn smaller and closer together the nearer they are to the vanishing point.

## LET'S EXPERIMENT
### HOLE IN YOUR HAND

**WE USUALLY SEE** through both eyes at the same time. We are not aware of seeing with two separate eyes, because our brains add the images from each eye together, as you will see in this experiment. **You will need:** a sheet of paper.

**1** Roll the paper into a tube and hold it with your right hand to your right eye. Look down the tube while keeping your left eye open.

**2** Position your left hand with the palm towards you against the tube, about two-thirds of the way down its length (as shown, right). You should now see a hole in your hand as your brain adds together the two separate images from each eye.

*Tube of paper*

### Holograms
Three-dimensional photos called holograms are created with lasers. One half of a laser beam is shone onto a special holographic film while the other half is scattered off the subject. The pattern of light recorded on the film where the beams meet represents both how bright and how far away from the film each part of the subject is. Shining a light at the developed film from a certain angle reveals a 3-D image.

# 2-D ILLUSIONS

Some optical illusions work because our brains do not have enough information to interpret properly what we are seeing. We fill in the missing pieces by guesswork based on our knowledge of the world around us. Other illusions occur when the surroundings of what we are looking at change. Colours can look different depending on what colours they are surrounded by, and shapes can seem altered with different backgrounds.

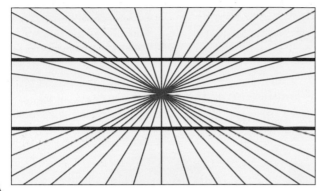

**Straight lines?**
The thick lines going across this drawing appear to bend outwards at the middle. In fact they are straight. You can prove this by putting a ruler up against them. It is the pattern of lines behind them that has tricked you into thinking they are curved.

**Moving circles?**
Pictures cannot really move about a page, but they can appear to move. Stare at the spot in the middle of these circles while moving the page towards then away from your eyes. The circles seem to rotate.

# STEREOGRAMS

We can see three dimensions because each of our eyes views an object from a different angle and produces a slightly different image of it. Our brains interpret these two images as a single image that not only has shape, but depth and distance as well. Pictures with hidden 3-D images are called stereograms (the one below creates a depth illusion). They are made by laying a two-dimensional, repeating pattern over a 3-D picture to disguise it. It can be difficult to see the hidden image. One way is to focus your eyes on a more distant object, then look at the stereogram without altering the focus of your eyes.

*Can you tell what this is?*

**Image recognition**
We identify different things because our brains compare what we see with images of objects stored in our memories. When a match occurs, we recognise whatever it is. If objects are blurred or disguised in some way, as in this picture, recognition becomes harder. If this picture was more heavily disguised, our brains might mistake it for something similar, such as a tiger.

# MORE THAN THE EYE CAN SEE

**THE HUMAN EYE CAN SEE A SURPRISINGLY LONG WAY** into the distance. Even neighbouring planets are visible on a clear night, although it is impossible to make out much detail without telescopes or binoculars. We cannot see details on very small things either, so use microscopes to reveal more about them or to see objects that are so small they are invisible to our unaided eyes. By using night-vision devices we can even see in the dark. Such devices amplify the small amounts of light present at night to produce a visible image.

**Naked-eye astronomy**
Before the invention of telescopes in the 17th century, astronomers observed the night sky unaided. This photograph shows Jupiter (top), Venus (centre) and the Moon (near the horizon) as they appear to the naked eye.

*The head of a fruit fly magnified 45 times*

## BINOCULARS

Like telescope lenses, the lenses in binoculars collect and magnify the light from objects. Light passes through the objective lenses, which produce an upside-down reversed image of the object (pp. 114–115). Inside the binoculars are specially shaped prisms that reflect light from two of their faces. There are two prisms in each half of a pair of binoculars. One prism turns the image up the right way, and the other turns it the right way round. The four successive reflections provide a long path for the light within a small space, allowing binoculars to be made much shorter and more portable than telescopes.

*Two prisms reflect the light.*

*Eyepiece lenses*

*Turning the focus adjustment knob brings the image into focus.*

*Light enters the binoculars by passing through the objective lens and heads towards the prisms.*

### Night vision
This picture of security police on a training exercise shows what an onlooker with a night-vision device could see. Night vision equipment amplifies the moonlight and starlight reflected from objects so they appear many times brighter. It does this by converting each photon (pp. 102–103) of light into an electron (pp. 42–43), then multiplying each electron into many more electrons. A screen at the end of the device then glows brightly whenever one of these electrons hits it, producing a visible image. Military personnel as well as nature and bird watchers use this type of powerful equipment.

### Hubble Space Telescope
The Earth's atmosphere distorts the images obtained by ground-based telescopes. By orbiting Earth above the atmosphere, the Hubble Space Telescope, launched in 1990, can obtain very clear images of stars and planets. This picture taken by Hubble shows a spiral galaxy 60 million light-years away. The outer stars are younger than those in the centre.

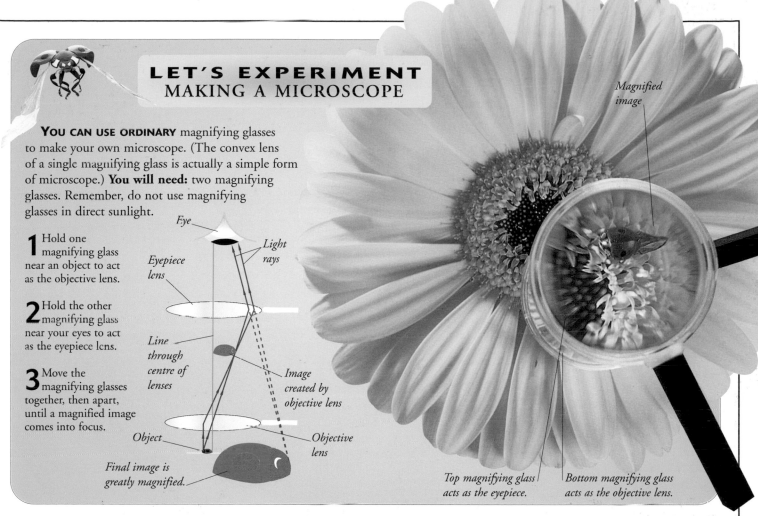

## LET'S EXPERIMENT
### MAKING A MICROSCOPE

**YOU CAN USE ORDINARY** magnifying glasses to make your own microscope. (The convex lens of a single magnifying glass is actually a simple form of microscope.) **You will need:** two magnifying glasses. Remember, do not use magnifying glasses in direct sunlight.

**1** Hold one magnifying glass near an object to act as the objective lens.

**2** Hold the other magnifying glass near your eyes to act as the eyepiece lens.

**3** Move the magnifying glasses together, then apart, until a magnified image comes into focus.

Eye

Light rays

Eyepiece lens

Line through centre of lenses

Image created by objective lens

Object

Objective lens

Final image is greatly magnified.

Magnified image

Top magnifying glass acts as the eyepiece.

Bottom magnifying glass acts as the objective lens.

## OPTICAL MICROSCOPE

Most optical microscopes are compound microscopes containing at least two lenses. These lenses are convex (curved outwards). The objective lens (or lenses) near to the specimen collects light reflected from it and forms a magnified image. The eyepiece lens (or lenses) that scientists look through then magnifies the image even more. Magnifications up to about 1,000 times are possible. The picture on the right shows onion cells magnified 330 times by an optical microscope.

### The first microscopes
English physicist Robert Hooke (1635–1703) carried out experiments with compound microscopes like this replica (below) of his design. In 1665 he published a book called *Micrographia* containing drawings of what he saw through his microscope, including this illustration of the stinging spines on a nettle leaf. Around this time, Dutch microscopist Anton van Leeuwenhoek (1632–1723) made hundreds of simple microscopes and used them to discover many new things, including bacteria.

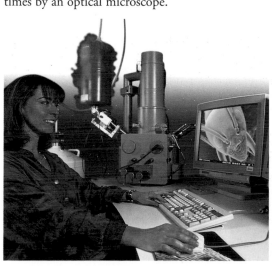

### Electron microscope
To magnify things hundreds of thousands of times, electron microscopes, which use beams of electrons rather than light, are needed. Very small objects cannot be seen through optical microscopes. Light won't reflect off the specimen because the length of the light waves is much larger than the object. However, tiny objects can interact with electron beams, which behave like incredibly small waves, to form images such as the one shown here of an ant's head.

Hooke's microscope screwed up and down for focusing.

Water-filled sphere helped focus light onto specimen.

Specimen mounted on metal spike

# PICTURE THIS

**WE CAN RECORD IMAGES OF** objects using a camera. Cameras work in a similar way to our eyes. All cameras have a lens to focus the light reflected from objects, a film (or rows of electronic devices) on which to record the image, and a system for controlling the amount of light that falls on the film. In order to see the photographs taken with a camera, the film must be developed and printed. French inventor Joseph Niepce (1765–1833) took the first permanent photograph in 1826 on a pewter plate coated with light-sensitive bitumen. Modern film has a coating of silver salts to record the image.

*High-speed action photo*

Shutter release button

Viewfinder

Aperture controls amount of light in camera

Solid lines show path of light rays.

Film

Dotted line shows light falling onto film when mirror moves and shutter opens.

Retractable mirror

Lens

## SLR CAMERA

All cameras have the same basic parts, but there are many different designs. In the single-lens reflex (SLR) camera, small mirrors and a prism reflect the image produced by the lens onto the viewfinder, so that it is exactly the same as the image that will be recorded. When the shutter-release button is pressed, the mirror moves out of the path of the light coming from the lenses and the shutter in front of the film opens. Light now falls onto the film at the back of the camera, recording the image. In many cameras, the image that is produced by the lens and recorded is not quite the exact image seen through the viewfinder.

Image formed on retina, which the brain interprets the right way up.

Light rays entering eye

Pupil

Retina

Image formed on film

Iris

Lens

Optic nerve to brain

Viewfinder

Adjustable aperture

Lens

Light rays entering camera

## EYE VERSUS CAMERA

A camera has much in common with the human eye. In the human eye, the muscles in the iris cause the small hole in the middle (the pupil) to contract in bright light or enlarge in dim light. A camera has a hole called an aperture that can be made larger or smaller to control the amount of light entering through the lens. The lens in the eye focuses light rays onto a light sensitive layer at the back of the eye called the retina. Cells in the retina send signals along the optic nerve to the brain, which interprets them as an image. In a camera, the lens focuses light onto a film, and the image is revealed when the film is printed.

### Digital photography

Light entering a digital camera is focused onto rows of small electronic devices at the back of a digital camera where the film would normally be. These devices convert the light into electronic signals which are saved onto a memory card in the camera. A small liquid-crystal display at the back of the camera acts as a viewfinder, and allows pictures in the memory to be viewed. Pictures taken on digital cameras can be stored on computer discs, viewed on a computer screen, and printed out.

**MAKE A SIMPLE MODEL CAMERA** to show how a real camera works. Your model camera will form an image in a similar way to a real camera, but it will not be able to make a photograph. **You will need**: cardboard box (such as a tissue box); scissors; cardboard tube (from loo roll or kitchen roll); pen; adhesive tape; tracing paper; magnifying glass.

**1** Carefully cut the bottom off the cardboard box. Hold the cardboard tube against the opposite side of the box and draw around it to make a circle.

**2** Carefully, cut out the circle in the box. Fit the tube into the circular hole so that about 5 cm (2 in) sticks out of the top of your box. Tape in position.

**3** Tape tracing paper over the large opening in the bottom of the box. This is where you will see the image.

**4** The magnifying glass provides the lens for the camera. Hold it near the end of the tube and focus by moving the magnifying glass nearer and farther from the tube.

**5** Find a well-lit object to look at. Hold the model camera so that you are looking at the end with the tracing paper.

**6** An upside-down and back to front image of the object will form on the tracing paper. If the image is out of focus, try moving the magnifying glass until you see a sharp image. In a real camera, this image would be formed on photographic film.

*Cardboard tube fits into hole in box.*

*The magnifying glass acts as the lens.*

*An upside-down image is formed on the tracing paper.*

# PROCESSING PICTURES

Photographic film is coated with a light-sensitive emulsion containing silver salts. Light falling on the emulsion causes a chemical change in the salts. The first stage of film processing creates a record of these changes. The film is soaked in developing chemicals that convert the exposed silver salts into metallic silver. A fixing solution washes away the unexposed silver salts, leaving a negative image that is darkest where the brightest light fell onto the film. Light is then shone through the negative onto photographic paper. The paper makes a print that is brightest where the negative is darkest, reproducing the photographed scene.

*Lens*

*Viewfinder*

*Finished Polaroid print*

## Colour negatives

Colour film has three layers of emulsion, one for each primary colour of light – blue, green, and red. During developing, each layer produces a dye of the opposite (complementary) colour to the light that fell on the film – yellow dye for the blue layer, magenta for the green layer and cyan for the red layer. Each dye in the negative absorbs light of its complementary colour. After printing, the complementary colours formed by the dyes in the paper absorb and reflect the colours in white light. This results in the original colours of the subject.

## Polaroid pictures

Instant photographs are available with a Polaroid camera. The American inventor Edwin Land (1909–1991) demonstrated the Polaroid camera in 1947. It uses a special type of film that is combined with printing paper. Developing chemicals are stored in packets between the negative and print layers of the Polaroid film. Once the film has been exposed, it passes through rollers which burst the storage packets and release the developing chemicals. Modern Polaroid cameras produce pictures in less than a minute.

# MOTION PICTURES

**A MOVIE IS MADE UP OF A SEQUENCE OF STILL**
pictures. The continuous movement seen on the screen
is an illusion. The human brain remembers an image
for about a tenth of a second after the image disappears.
This effect is called persistence of vision. When two
pictures appear in quick succession, persistence of
vision causes the first picture to blend into the second,
appearing as a single moving image. The still pictures
that make up a movie are called frames. At the cinema,
24 frames per second are projected onto the screen.
The frames blend together, creating the illusion of a
continuous moving image – a movie.

## EARLY CINEMA

The American inventor George Eastman (1854–1932)
brought flexible film onto the market in 1889. A year
later, William Dickson (1860–1935), an assistant to
the American inventor Thomas Edison, developed a
way of moving this film through cameras and
projectors. He punched tiny holes down the sides,
so that metal claws could pull the film along. The first
motion picture to be screened for the public was
shown in Paris in 1895. It was a silent movie made
by French brothers Auguste (1862–1954) and Louis
Lumière (1864–1948). Early films had only 16 frames
per second. This meant that the pictures seemed to
flicker on the screen, instead of blending into a
continuously moving image. In 1927, *The Jazz Singer*,
starring Al Jolson, became the first "talking"
feature film, adding sound to moving images.

*An early movie
recorded on
Eastman's film.*

**Blue screen effects**
Amazing special effects
can be created on film
with the help of a giant blue
screen. First, the scene is filmed
in front of the blue screen. A computer is
then used to remove the blue and replace it with
another background that has been filmed separately.
These pictures show a scene from the film *The Perfect
Storm* (2000). The actors were filmed on the boat
against a giant blue screen. Then the blue was
replaced by a raging storm in the background
to create the final scene (inset).

## LET'S EXPERIMENT
### MAKE A FLICK BOOK

**MAKE YOUR OWN** simple motion picture.
**You will need:** small notebook; pen.

**1** Draw a picture on the top page.
Change the picture slightly on
the following pages to create a sense
of movement. For example, to make
this figure wave his arm, copy your
original drawing several times
over, moving the arm slightly
higher in each picture.

**2** Flick the pages of the
notebook. The figure
appears to be waving in a
continuous moving image
because your brain blends
the pictures together.

*Draw the
pictures on the
right-hand
pages only.*

## IMAX CINEMAS

Most films are shot on 35mm film, but IMAX
films are recorded on 70mm film, which has
frames ten times bigger than normal. IMAX
screens are curved so that the picture fills the
viewer's entire field of vision. Some IMAX films
are three dimensional (3-D). Human brains
combine the separate images from our eyes into
a single image that has depth and shape. A 3-D
camera mimics this by recording images from two
lenses. The movie is projected by switching from
the "left eye" film to the "right eye" film 96 times
per second. Viewers wear special headsets that
stop light reaching the right eye while the left
eye image is on the screen and vice versa.
The result is a lifelike, 3-D film experience.

*The outline shows all of the squirrel's features.*

# ANIMATION

Thousands of drawings are needed to make our favourite cartoon characters come to life. A cartoon feature film contains about 65,000 pictures. Animators draw the characters in different stages of motion onto pieces of transparent film called cels. A succession of these transparent cels are laid over the top of a background drawing which remains the same. For each sequence, animators draw the extremes of movement first, like the take-off and landing of this squirrel, before completing the in-between stages. The outline of the character is drawn on the front of each cel, then the colour is painted onto the back.

*Colours must be consistent throughout.*

*Shifting the background behind the cel is another way of giving the character a sense of motion.*

*Extremes of movement are drawn first.*

*Finished cel*

### 3-D animation

Like 3-D film, 3-D animation adds visual depth to the images. Modelling clay is used to create characters like the one shown on the left. Each frame is filmed separately so that the position of the limbs and facial expressions can be changed slightly in between, giving the impression of continuous movement in the film. Some models have a range of cable or radio controlled motors, allowing the puppeteer to move them via remote control during normal filming. Models are also used in ordinary films to create special effects.

*Wire frame image of CGi character*

# COMPUTER ANIMATION

Many films now use computer generated images (CGi) to create different effects. To produce a CGi character like this dragon from the film *Dragonheart* (1997), a 3-D representation called a wire frame is created on a computer (see right). This acts like a skeleton for the character. Muscles are added to the digital skeleton, then colour and fine detail put on top. Computer software enables the CGi character to move in a realistic way. Separately filmed background footage can be combined with the CGi later (see below) to create the finished scene.

# WAVES AND COLOURS

**LIGHT TRAVELS IN THE FORM OF TINY WAVES.**
These light waves have peaks and troughs like waves on the sea. The distance between two peaks is known as the wavelength. Different colours are different wavelengths of visible light. However, white light, such as sunlight, is not just a single wavelength. The famous English scientist Isaac Newton (1642–1727) discovered that sunlight is made up of the spectrum of colours that we see in a rainbow – red, orange, yellow, green, blue, indigo, and violet. Red has the longest wavelength, while violet has the shortest.

*Wavelength of red light*

*Wavelength of violet light*

**Comparative wavelengths of red and violet light**

## SPLITTING SUNLIGHT

When sunlight shines on a triangular block of glass called a prism, we can see that it is made up of a combination of different coloured light waves. The prism bends (refracts) the beam of sunlight. Each colour is refracted by a slightly different amount, separating the sunlight into the familiar spectrum of red, orange, yellow, green, blue, indigo, and violet.

*A beam of sunlight shines onto a prism.*

*Some light is reflected by the bottom of the prism.*

# NEWTON'S PRISMS

Isaac Newton discovered the light spectrum in 1665 by conducting an experiment similar to the one shown below. (Read the diagram from right to left.) Sunlight shines through a slit in the window shutters and onto a prism. The prism splits the sunlight into the seven colours of the spectrum. The separated light waves then pass through a lens that focuses them onto a second (upside-down) prism. There, the colours recombine to produce another beam of white light. As the beam passes through a third (right-way-up) prism, the light disperses yet again, displaying the colour spectrum onto the screen. When Newton blocked out individual colours before they reached the lens, he noticed that these colours did not appear in the final spectrum on the screen.

1. Sunlight shines through slit in window shutters.
2. First prism
3. Lens
4. Second prism
5. Third prism
6. Screen
*Fig 16.*

This diagram from Newton's book, *Opticks*, published in 1704, shows the dispersion and recombination of the light spectrum.

# INTERFERENCE

The changing colours of certain objects are produced by interference. These colours are called iridescent. For example, a compact disc has tiny grooves that separate a ray of light into hundreds of smaller beams. Where these beams meet, they interfere with each other. If constructive interference occurs for a particular colour, the light waves combine and become brighter. If destructive interference occurs, this colour is cancelled out. When viewed from different angles, the colours change. Soap bubbles have iridescent colours that are created when the light reflected by the outer surface interferes with the light reflected by the inner surface.

*The prism bends the light.*

*The light separates into the colours of the spectrum.*

## Stellar spectra

The colour of light often indicates temperature. For instance, we can tell how hot a star is by its colour. The hottest stars are blue, while the coolest are red. Yellow stars like our Sun are in between, with a surface temperature of approximately 5,500°C (9,900°F). Most light emitted by a star is of a particular wavelength, but other colours do appear in the spectrum. Astronomers can analyse the spectrum to find out which chemical elements are present (below).

**YOU CAN DO THIS VERSION** of Newton's spectrum experiment in front of a window at home. **You will need**: piece of card; scissors; straight-sided glass filled with water; adhesive tape; white paper. For the best results, carry out the experiment on a sunny day. You can also use a torch beam instead of sunlight, although the spectrum will not be as clear.

**1** Cut a long vertical slit in the piece of card. Tape the card to the glass of water. (The glass of water will produce the same effect as a prism.) Stand the glass on a sheet of paper placed in front of a window, so that sunlight shines through the slit in the card and onto the glass.

**2** The sunlight coming through the slit is refracted by the glass of water. Each colour in the beam of sunlight is refracted by a slightly different amount, causing a spectrum to appear on the paper.

*A spectrum forms on the paper.*

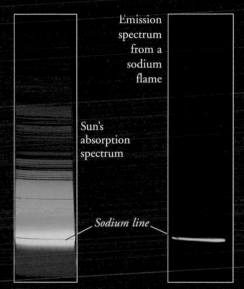

Emission spectrum from a sodium flame

Sun's absorption spectrum

*Sodium line*

## Spectroscopy

Different types of atoms absorb and emit different colours of light, so a spectrum can be used to identify elements in a substance. An absorption spectrum is obtained by shining a white light through a substance, then splitting the light into a spectrum. Dark lines on the spectrum represent atoms that absorb that specific colour. The Sun's spectrum (above left) shows several dark lines. One line shows an absorption of yellow light by sodium in the Sun's outer layers. An emission spectrum shows the colour of light emitted from a substance. A sodium flame gives off yellow light, as shown in this emission spectrum (above right).

## RAINBOWS

When there is sunshine and rain at the same time, a rainbow may appear. Sunlight is bent (refracted) as it enters a raindrop. It is then reflected off the back of the raindrop before being refracted again as it leaves the drop. Each colour in the white sunlight bends by a slightly different amount as it enters and leaves the drop. This splits the sunlight into the familiar colours of the spectrum – red, orange, yellow, green, blue, indigo, and violet. Occasionally, you can see a double rainbow with a fainter, secondary rainbow outside the primary one. The secondary rainbow forms when sunlight enters the bottom of the raindrops instead of the top. The sunlight is then reflected twice off the inner surface of the drop, which means that the order of the colours in a secondary rainbow are reversed.

Primary rainbow

*Dispersed light is reflected*

*Sunlight enters the top of the raindrop*

*Reflected light leaves raindrop*

Secondary rainbow

*Light reflected a second time*

*Reflected light leaves raindrop*

*Sunlight enters the bottom of the raindrop*

*Dispersed light is reflected*

**Light beam**

**Red, blue, and green produce white light.**

**Blue and green produce cyan.**

**Red and green produce yellow.**

**Red and blue produce magenta.**

# MIXING COLOURS

**WHITE LIGHT IS MADE UP OF ALL** the colours in the spectrum (pp. 118–119). It is also possible to make white simply by adding together the three primary colours of light – red, blue, and green. Amazingly, by combining these primary colours in different proportions, you can produce any colour you wish. This process is known as "colour addition", and it is how a range of colours is produced on television screens. However, unless an object is a source of light, for example a torch, it does not give out its own distinct colour. The things that surround us appear to be coloured because they reflect a single colour or a mixture of colours back to our eyes from the white light that falls on them, while absorbing all other colours. Paints and pigments work in the same way. Forming colours like this is called "colour subtraction" because colours are taken away from white light to make the colour that we can see.

## PRIMARY COLOURS OF LIGHT

Red, blue, and green are the primary colours of light. Combinations of these three primary colours can make any other colour (see above). A mixture of red light and green light gives yellow, while mixing blue light and red light makes magenta. Blue light and green light together produce a bright turquoise blue called cyan. Varying the amounts of each light in any mixture allows many more colours to be produced. Mixing all three primary colours together in equal amounts produces white light. Colour addition like this is used to produce the different colours on the screens of colour televisions.

## COLOUR VISION

Light is focused on the retina inside the eyes, and millions of light-sensitive cells send signals along the optic nerve to the brain. Rods and cones are the two main types of such cells. Rods work in dim light and cannot detect colour. Cones come in three types – one responds to blue light, another to red, and the third to green. As these are the primary colours of light, all other colours can be seen as they stimulate different combinations of cones. Not everyone can see all colours. People who are colour blind have defective cones, so they confuse colours. Colour blindness can be diagnosed using tests like this picture (above). People who cannot see the difference between red and green do not see the number 683.

**Television**
Tiny dots or strips of phosphor are arranged all over colour television screens in groups of three (left). In each group, one dot will emit red light, another blue, and the remaining one green. Varying the amounts of each of these primary colours of light creates a full range of different colours when the screen is viewed from a distance.

**YOU CAN SHOW THAT** white light is made up of a mixture of colours. Each colour painted on a disc will reflect a different colour of light. When you spin the disc, these colours will mix together to produce white. **You will need:** piece of card; saucer; pencil; scissors; protractor; coloured paints; pencil sharpener.

**1** Place the saucer on the piece of card and draw around it. Carefully cut out the disc, and use a protractor to divide it into seven equal segments.

**2** Colour in the segments with the colours of the spectrum in the order that they appear in a rainbow – red, orange, yellow, green, blue, indigo, and violet.

**3** Sharpen the pencil and carefully push it through the centre of the disc. Position the disc halfway along the pencil's length.

**4** Stand the pencil on its point and use the other end to spin the disc as quickly as possible. The colours merge together and the disc looks almost white.

*Coloured cardboard disc before spinning*

*The colours disappear as the disc spins.*

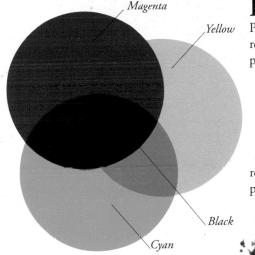

*Magenta*

*Yellow*

*Black*

*Cyan*

# PRIMARY COLOURS OF PIGMENTS

Pigments absorb certain colours from the light that falls on them and reflect others. Magenta, cyan, and yellow are the primary colours of pigments, and each absorbs one of the primary colours of light. For example, yellow pigment absorbs blue but reflects green and red light, which our brains add together so we see yellow. Different combinations of primary pigments produce every colour except white. If equal amounts of all three primary pigments are mixed together, they absorb all three primary colours of light and we see black (left). When painting, red, blue, and yellow are used as primary colours instead.

*Cadmium red*

*Viridian*

*Cadmium yellow*

### Natural dyes and pigments

Many of the dyes and pigments that we use today are artificially created, but in the past they were made from natural substances. The earliest cave paintings used colours made from ground-up rocks and clays, charcoal, and chalk. Cave painters only used a limited range of colours – mainly reds and browns – but by the Middle Ages a much larger variety of dyes and pigments had been discovered. Many were made from crushed minerals, which produced vivid colours. Viridian, for example, is a bluish-green mineral called chromium oxide found in a type of clay called "terre verte". Cadmium yellow is a bright yellow pigment that contains the metallic compound cadmium sulphide.

# ELECTRICITY AND MAGNETISM

**Picture:** *Lightning bolts strike Tucson, USA. Lightning occurs when electrical charge builds up in clouds.*

# THE RIGHT CONNECTION

**PEOPLE HAVE BEEN AWARE OF THE**
forces of electricity and magnetism for a
very long time. The ancient Greeks carried
out electrical experiments. They were also
aware of naturally magnetic rocks. As early
as the 11th century, it is thought that
magnetism was used in China to help
with navigation. However, it was only
in the 19th century that a link was
discovered between electricity and
magnetism, and the power of
electricity could be put to use.
Electricity is the major source
of power for much of the world
today, and enables electronic
devices and computers to work.

*3-D MRI scan (with false
colours) of a human
brain as viewed
from above*

*The word "electricity"
comes from the
Greek word for
amber – elektron.
If rubbed with wool
or fur, amber becomes
electrically charged and
can attract light objects.*

## MRI SCANS

Magnetism has many useful applications.
For example, doctors can produce pictures
of the insides of our bodies through a
technique called magnetic resonance
imaging (MRI). The patient is placed in a
large magnetic field. About 65 per cent of
the human body is made from water. The
magnetic field allows the hydrogen atoms
in this water to absorb high frequency
radio waves in a certain way. When the
radio waves are switched off, the hydrogen
atoms emit the energy they have absorbed
as much weaker radio waves. Each type of
tissue emits
waves of different
lengths and strengths.
A computer turns the
radio waves into images
that help to diagnose diseases.

## PACEMAKERS

The human heartbeat is triggered by tiny
electrical impulses from an area of the
heart called the pacemaker. If the impulses
are impaired, an artificial pacemaker can be
implanted in the chest. This has a battery
that enables it to produce the required
electrical impulses. A machine called an
electrocardiograph monitors the electrical
activity of our hearts via sensors placed on
the body. Problems with the heart show up
as changes in the electrocardiogram (ECG),
which is the wavy line made by the machine.
and coronal mass ejections. The huge and

**c. 600 BC** Greek philosopher and astronomer Thales of Miletus discovers that rubbing amber produces an electrical charge.

**c. 1000** It is believed that the magnetic compass is invented in China.

**1600** English scientist and physician William Gilbert tries to explain the magnetic properties of Earth.

**1729** English scientists Stephen Gray and Jean Desaguliers discover that some substances are electrical insulators, while others are electrical conductors.

**1752** American scientist and statesman Benjamin Franklin discovers the electrical nature of lightning.

**1820** Danish physicist Hans Christian Oersted discovers the link between electricity and magnetism.

## MAGNETIC STORMS

The Sun constantly gives out a stream of charged particles into space called the solar wind. Sometimes the Sun has violent reactions on its surface called solar flares

*Certain types of eruption on the Sun can cause magnetic storms on Earth.*

and coronal mass ejections. The huge numbers of high-energy particles emitted in these explosions produce a disturbance in the Earth's magnetic field. This is known as a magnetic storm. Magnetic storms can damage satellites and cause huge surges of electricity in power transmission lines that can blow out power stations. They also interfere with radio reception and cause compass needles to change direction.

## ELECTRONIC DEVICES

Many familiar electrical devices, from televisions to microwave ovens, contain components that work by using varying

*A simple type of electronic toy*

electrical signals to represent information. These components are electronic devices. In 1947, the invention of an electronic device called a transistor enabled electronic goods to be made small enough to be practical. In some electronic equipment,

such as the game shown below left, all of the electronic components needed to work the device are contained on a tiny piece of silicon known as a chip. More complicated equipment usually contains several chips, along with separate electronic components mounted on a printed circuit board.

## TRANSDUCERS

Electronic systems contain devices called transducers. Transducers change one form of energy into another form. They can change electrical energy to mechanical energy or mechanical energy into electrical energy, for example. Microphones and loudspeakers are examples of transducers. A microphone contains a diaphragm that is mechanically vibrated by sound waves. The vibrating movement causes a fluctuating electric current to be produced that represents the original sound waves. In a loudspeaker, the reverse occurs, with alterations in an electric current from the amplifier causing a diaphragm to vibrate and produce sound waves.

*Microphone components*

## COMPUTERS

It is hard to imagine a world without computers and the Internet, but computers have only been available for personal use since the mid-1970s. Since then, there have been huge advances in processing speed and much larger amounts of data can be stored in a computer's memory. These advances continue today. Computers have many uses, from helping engineers design bridges and buildings to predicting the weather. Computers store and process information in the form of binary digits (bits). These bits have only

*Laptop computers enable us to work almost anywhere.*

two possible values – "0" and "1". Many computers currently process information one step at a time. Scientists are hoping to build much faster quantum computers in the future that can compute several possibilities simultaneously.

## PARTICLE ACCELERATORS

For some experiments, physicists need to accelerate charged sub-atomic particles to incredibly high speeds. They use huge pieces of scientific equipment called particle accelerators to do this. Electricity makes the particles accelerate, while magnetic fields keep the particles on the correct path as they speed along inside the accelerator. By studying what happens when these high-speed particles hit atoms or other particles, scientists can learn more about the structure and nature of the atoms and particles.

*Tunnel housing two particle accelerators at Fermilab in the USA*

**1823** English mathematician Charles Babbage begins designing mechanical computing machine.

**1831** English physicist and chemist Michael Faraday discovers that magnetism can be used to produce electricity.

**1876** Scottish inventor Alexander Graham Bell patents the telephone.

**1911** Dutch physicist Heike Kamerlingh-Onnes discovers superconductivity.

**1947** American physicists John Bardeen, Walter Brattain, and (British-born) William Shockley invent the transistor.

**1958** American electronics engineer Jack Kilby produces the first integrated circuit.

**1958** American company Bell introduces modems.

# ELECTRICITY AT REST

**WHEN WE THINK OF ELECTRICITY, WE IMAGINE** it flowing through electrical devices. However, electricity does not always move. Static electricity causes lightning strikes and makes some clothes crackle as we take them off. Objects can develop a positive or a negative charge when they rub against each other. The rubbing knocks electrons, which have a negative charge, off the atoms in one object so it becomes positively charged, while the other object is negatively charged as freed electrons move to its atoms. Although static electricity is often undesirable, it is put to good use inside photocopiers.

## LIGHTNING

Water and ice particles inside thunderclouds collide and become charged with static electricity. Smaller positively charged particles move to the top of the cloud, while heavier ones with a negative charge collect at the bottom. The negative charge from the base of the cloud induces a positive charge on the ground beneath. If it is strong enough, the charge in the cloud forces its way through the air to the ground and discharges as lightning.

**Franklin's lightning experiment**
The American statesman Benjamin Franklin (1706–1790) proved that lightning was static electricity by performing a dangerous experiment (above). He attached a key to the string of a kite, then flew the kite in a thunderstorm. The wet string acted as a conductor, so when he brought his hand near the key he felt a shock and saw sparks like those in laboratory experiments on static electricity.

Original document

"Electrical" copy on drum

The photocopy

Heated rollers bond the toner to the paper.

Statically charged drum

Paper is fed through to the drum.

Stack of copy paper

# PHOTOCOPIER

When someone presses the "copy" button on a photocopier, light is shone at the document. The light reflects off the white areas of the page but not off the parts covered with ink. A metal drum inside the machine is charged with static electricity. Wherever light reflected from the document falls on this drum, it neutralizes the charge. This leaves the drum charged up only in the areas where the ink was on the original document. The drum is coated with toner (powdered ink), which only sticks to the charged parts. When the drum spins, the toner is transferred onto paper, which is also charged, to make the copy.

## Van de Graaff generator

Static electricity can be built up using a Van de Graaff generator, which was invented by American physicist Robert Van de Graaff (1901–1967). A small version of this machine (above) produces amazing effects. When someone touches the metal dome, negative electrical charges pass through them. As the strands of their hair become charged, they stand on end because like charges repel each other.

## Anti-static clothing

Static electricity can be uncomfortable when it makes clothing stick to us (above) and crackle as we take it off. When we move, opposite charges can build up on our bodies and the garments we are wearing, making them cling to us. Anti-static yarns help to drain away the charge or prevent charge build-up, reducing these effects.

## LET'S EXPERIMENT
## MAKE AN ELECTROSCOPE

**YOU CAN BUILD** an electroscope to measure static electric charges. **You will need:** an adult's help; foil biscuit wrapper; drinking glass; piece of card; pencil; scissors; wire (cut from a coathanger); glue; adhesive tape; plastic pen; some silk.

**1** Flatten the foil, and cut out a long rectangular piece to act as the leaves of the electroscope. Roll the remaining foil into a ball.

**2** Place the glass upside down on the card. Draw round it, then carefully cut out the disc.

**3** Push the wire carefully through the middle of the disc and glue it in place. Ask an adult to bend the end of the wire. Suspend the leaves from it using a drop of glue. Lower the wire into the glass, and tape the card disc to the rim. Push the foil ball onto the end of the wire.

**4** Rub the pen with the silk to give it a positive charge. Hold it near the foil ball. Negative charges in the wire are attracted towards the ball, which gives the leaves of the electroscope a positive charge. As they have the same charge, the leaves repel each other.

Positively charged pen

Negative charge moves up the wire towards the ball.

Like charges on the leaves make them move apart.

# ELECTRICITY THAT FLOWS

**MANY MACHINES REQUIRE A CONTINUOUS FLOW OF** electricity, known as an electric current. Static electricity (pp. 126–127) cannot be used to power electrical devices. The simplest way of generating an electric current is provided by a battery, which is a useful and portable source of power. Some batteries, such as those in cars, are rechargeable so they can be used again and again. Materials that electric currents can flow through are known as electrical conductors. Metals are particularly good conductors, so electrical wires are made of metal.

*Lead electrode*

*Terminal*

*Plate separator*

*Lead oxide plate*

*All the plates are immersed in sulphuric acid.*

## ELECTRIC CURRENT

A current is a flow of electric charge that occurs when electrons that are free to move inside a conductor – usually a metal – travel in a particular way. Normally the electrons move randomly in different directions (right). However, if the conductor is connected to a battery, the electrons, which have a negative charge, flow towards the battery's positive terminal, and a current is produced (inset). The rate of flow of electric charge is measured using a device called an ammeter.

*Electrons flowing in one direction produce an electric current.*

*Electrons moving randomly produce no current.*

## BATTERIES

All batteries contain two metal electrodes separated by a conducting mixture called an electrolyte. The mixture causes a chemical reaction at each electrode, which produces a current. The batteries in torches and radios are known as dry batteries. They contain a carbon rod and a zinc cylinder separated by a conducting paste. The chemical reaction in a dry battery eventually ceases, and the battery stops working. However, some batteries can be recharged by applying an electric current that reverses the chemical reaction. Cars contain rechargeable lead-acid batteries (above) that supply current to start the engine.

### The first battery

The Italian physicist Alessandro Volta (1745–1827) built the first practical battery in 1800. His "voltaic pile" (right) was based on three types of disc. A zinc disc and a copper disc were separated by a pasteboard disc that had been soaked in salt solution or weak acid. The zinc and copper discs acted as electrodes and the moist pasteboard as the electrolyte. Volta stacked up several sets of these discs to produce a greater amount of electricity.

*Copper disc*

*Zinc disc*

*Pasteboard disc*

---

## LET'S EXPERIMENT
### MAKING A BATTERY

**YOU CAN MAKE** a working battery. **You will need:** an adult present; vinegar; glass container; electrical wire with metal clips on the ends; strip of zinc; strip of copper; small 3-volt light bulb.

**1** Pour some vinegar into the container. Connect a lead to the end of each strip. Clip the other ends of these leads to either side of the bulb as shown. Immerse the strips in the vinegar.

**2** A chemical reaction starts to dissolve the zinc strip. Electrons from the zinc atoms collect on the strip, making it negative. These flow through the completed circuit to the copper strip, which has become positively charged by losing electrons to the acid. The bulb lights as the current flows.

*Heating elements from an electric fire are made from conducting wire.*

# CONDUCTORS

Materials containing atoms with one or more electrons that are free to move can conduct electricity and are known as conductors. Materials whose electrons cannot move around are unable to conduct electricity and are known as insulators. Semiconducting materials also exist (pp. 144–145). Metals are especially good conductors as they have large numbers of free electrons. The cables that connect electrical devices to electricity supplies are made from conducting metal wire – usually copper – surrounded by an insulator such as rubber or plastic. The insulator ensures that the current only flows through the conductor and cannot harm anyone who touches the cable.

*Ammeter*

*Resistor*

### Measuring current
There are several different types of ammeter used for measuring electric currents. One is based on the fact that an electric current produces a magnetic field. This field deflects a needle, which points to a different position on a scale, depending on the strength of the current. Another type measures how much the current heats up a thin wire inside the ammeter. Most modern ammeters have a digital display instead of a mechanical pointer.

## LET'S EXPERIMENT
### TESTING FOR CONDUCTORS

**YOU CAN USE A BATTERY** and a light bulb to discover whether or not a material conducts electricity. Handle batteries with care and always follow instructions. **You will need:** an adult present; electrical leads with metal clips on the ends; 9-volt battery; small light bulb; items to test (for example, a piece of string, a wooden ruler, a screwdriver, a fork).

**1** Connect the leads to the terminals of the battery. Clip one lead to the light bulb, then connect the other side of the light bulb to one end of the test object as shown.

**2** Next clip the other lead from the battery to the opposite end of the test object to form a complete circuit. If the object is a conductor, the bulb will light up. If the object is an electrical insulator, the bulb will remain unlit.

*A selection of objects to test*

*Conductors light the bulb.*

# ELECTRICAL CIRCUITS

**ELECTRICITY WILL ONLY FLOW IF IT HAS A COMPLETE** circuit to go round. The three basic components of a circuit are a conductor for the electricity to flow through (such as copper wire), something for the circuit to power (for example a light bulb), and an energy source to drive the current (such as a battery). Once a circuit is complete, electricity will only stop flowing if the circuit is broken or the energy runs out. Switches allow the current to be turned off when it is not needed. Scientists use standard symbols to represent the components of electrical circuits in circuit diagrams (drawings).

*Switch*

*Light bulb*

*Battery*

**Symbols of a simple circuit**

*Tungsten filament*

## RESISTANCE

All conductors have a certain amount of resistance to the flow of current. For example, around 10 per cent of the power from electricity generating stations is lost before it reaches homes and industries because of resistance by the transmission cables. When a conductor resists an electric current, the electrical energy is turned into heat. This effect is made use of in many domestic electrical appliances. Electronic devices called resistors (right), which are made from materials that have high resistance, are used in many circuits to control the current in various ways.

### Heating and lighting

Appliances such as cookers and irons have heating elements made from conducting wire that has a high resistance to electric current. As the element resists the current flowing through it, it gets hot. The same principle enables an electric light bulb to produce light. Light bulbs contain a filament made of tungsten, which has very high resistance. When electricity passes through the filament, it becomes so hot that it glows white.

*Metal contact*

---

## LET'S EXPERIMENT
## SIMPLE CIRCUITS

**YOU CAN SEE HOW** simple circuits work using some basic equipment. Handle batteries with care and always follow instructions. **You will need:** an adult present; a 9-volt battery; some leads with metal clips on the ends; two small light bulbs; paper clips.

**1** To set up a series circuit, connect the bulbs to the battery so the circuit is a continuous loop (right). Use a paper clip to switch the current on and off. Both lamps only light dimly, as the resistance of the bulbs reduces the amount of current passing through the circuit. If your circuit does not work at first, check that there is good contact between each of the wires and the components.

*Metal clip*

*Light bulb*

**Series circuit**

**Series circuit**

**Parallel circuit**

*One branch of the parallel circuit*

**2** To make a parallel circuit, you need to use two paper clips (left) to create two separate paths for the current. Connect a light bulb to each branch of the circuit. The resistance in each branch is halved compared with the series circuit because there is only one lamp in it, so both bulbs will look much brighter.

**Parallel circuit**

# ELECTRICITY IN THE HOME

Houses that are connected to a mains electricity supply usually have at least two electrical circuits in the form of rings. The cables of each ring run through the rooms. The lighting ring main brings electricity to light fittings, while the power ring main supplies a higher current to wall sockets for electrical appliances. Some countries use a separate heavy-duty ring for the cooker and other kitchen appliances. There is a box where the mains enters the house containing a meter that records how much electricity is used and a fuse for each ring. It is dangerous to play with mains electrical sockets.

*Lighting ring main*

*Power ring main*

*Mains connection and fuse box*

### Fuses

If too high a current flows through a wire, it could overheat and start a fire. To prevent this, the plugs of all domestic electrical appliances, and the house ring mains circuits, have fuses fitted. Fuses (left) contain metal wires or strips that melt if more than a certain current passes through them. So if a fault develops in a particular circuit and too large a current flows round it, the fuse will "blow" and break the circuit.

### Superconductivity

When some materials are cooled to extremely low temperatures, they lose their resistance to electric current and become "superconductors". Many materials including tin, aluminium, and lead have shown superconductivity. The effect was first seen in mercury in 1911 by Dutch physicist Heike Kamerlingh Onnes. Mercury must be cooled below −269°C (−452°F) to become a superconductor. Electric currents on a superconductor's surface produce a magnetic field that can repel and levitate a small magnet (above).

# ELECTRONIC CIRCUITS

Many modern products including televisions and computers contain complex electronic circuits that enable them to work. Instead of being connected by wires, the electronic components in these circuits are usually attached to a printed circuit board (PCB) like the one shown below. PCBs are made from a layer of electrically insulating material coated with a conducting substance such as copper. The copper is removed in the places where it is not needed, leaving a pattern of connections between the various components. Electric currents can then flow along these copper tracks.

*Capacitor*

*Copper connection*

*Diode*

# ELECTRICAL CHEMISTRY

**WE TEND TO THINK OF ELECTRICAL CONDUCTORS AS** being solids, such as metal wires, but some liquids can also conduct electricity. When electricity is passed through a conducting liquid, called an electrolyte, a chemical reaction takes place. If the electrolyte is brine (salt and water), the electricity splits the solution into chlorine gas and sodium hydroxide (caustic soda). If the electrolyte is a solution containing a metal, the current will separate the metal out of the solution. This process is known as electrolysis. Today electrolysis has many uses, including extracting some metals from rough ores and coating objects with a thin layer of a precious metal.

## LAWS OF ELECTROLYSIS

Michael Faraday
1791–1867

The British physicist and chemist Michael Faraday carried out many detailed experiments on electrolysis and discovered two laws of electrolysis. Faraday's first law states that the mass of substances formed during electrolysis is proportional to the amount of electricity used. However, the amount of electricity needed to form each separate substance depends on the charge and the mass of the substance. Faraday's second law explains this scientific principle mathematically.

*Chemical plants manufacture chlorine by electrolysis.*

## ELECTROLYSIS

For electrolysis to take place, two conducting rods, called electrodes, are dipped into an electrolyte. The electrodes are connected by wires to a battery or similar electricity supply. The electrode connected to the negative battery terminal is called the cathode, and the electrode connected to the positive terminal is the anode. As the electrolyte is a conductor, electricity flows around the circuit. The atoms of an electrolyte have an electric charge and are known as ions. Positive ions (cations) are attracted to the cathode, while negative ions (anions) are attracted to the anode. Chemical reactions at the electrodes cause the ions to gain or lose electrons, splitting the electrolyte.

### Davy's experiment

In 1806, the British chemist Humphry Davy (1778–1829) predicted that electricity would be able to separate elements from compounds (pp. 44–45). The following year he used electrolysis to make pure potassium from potassium carbonate and pure sodium from sodium carbonate. Davy went on to produce barium, boron, calcium, and strontium by electrolysis. Today some metals, such as aluminium and magnesium, are extracted from their ores by electrolysis. Other metals, including copper, are purified using the technique.

*Sealed glass tube containing pure potassium*

**YOU CAN PROVE** that adding salt to water makes it a better electrical conductor. Handle batteries with care and always follow instructions. **You will need:** an adult present; electrical leads with metal clips on the ends; 9-volt battery; glass container; water; tape; small bulb; table salt; plastic spoon.

**1** Connect a lead to each battery terminal. Place the free end of one of the leads in the container of water, and tape the wire to the container. Connect the end of the other lead to the light bulb, then clip another lead to the other side of the bulb and place the free end of this lead in the water a few centimetres away from the first lead and tape it down.

**2** Slowly add salt to the water, stirring it in carefully without moving the leads. The bulb will light up more and more brightly as more salt is added. If you repeat the experiment with fresh water and add sugar instead of salt, the bulb will not light up because sugary water is not an electrolyte.

*Battery*

*Electrodes*

*The bulb glows brighter as more salt is added.*

*Salt water electrolyte*

# ELECTROPLATING

Electrolysis can be used to give objects a thin coating of metal around 0.05 mm (0.002 in) thick. This process, known as electroplating, is used to coat cutlery made from cheap metal with an expensive metal. For example, to silverplate a spoon it is first cleaned, then made into a cathode by being connected to the negative terminal of a battery. A silver bar is used as the anode, and both electrodes are dipped in a solution containing a silver compound. Positively charged silver ions from the solution are attracted to the negatively charged spoon, which ends up with an even coating of silver if it is rotated slowly.

**Nickel spoon**

**Silver-plated spoon**

### Rust proofing
Electroplating can be used to protect objects from corrosion. For example, car bodies can be electroplated with zinc to help prevent them from rusting. During the manufacturing process, the metal vehicle body is dipped into a huge bath containing a solution of zinc. The body is electrified so that it behaves like a cathode and attracts the positive zinc ions from the solution. The ions quickly cover every part of the car, leaving it with a coating of zinc.

# MAGNETISM

**ALL MAGNETS ARE SURROUNDED BY A FORCE FIELD THAT IS STRONGEST** at the "poles" (the ends) of the magnet. Poles can be "north" or "south". Opposite magnetic poles attract each other, while like magnetic poles (for example, two south poles) repel each other. The Earth produces a magnetic field and behaves as if it has a huge magnet inside it. The south pole of this imaginary magnet is near the geographical North Pole at a point known as the magnetic north pole. Compasses always point north because the north poles of their needles are attracted to the Earth's internal south pole.

## EARTH'S MAGNETIC FIELD

The Earth's core consists of solid iron surrounded by liquid iron. Electric currents flowing in the outer core are thought to produce the Earth's magnetic field. Scientists are uncertain how these currents are generated, but they are probably linked to the Earth's rotation. The Earth's magnetic field extends out into space, and any particles entering a region known as the magnetosphere will be affected by it. Over long periods of time, the Earth's magnetic poles slowly move. This means that at some points in history the magnetic south pole has been in the magnetic north pole's present position. This computer simulation (right) shows the Earth's magnetic poles changing position over thousands of years.

## COMPASSES

One of the easiest ways to find out which direction you are facing is to use a magnetic compass. The compass needle always points towards the magnetic north pole, but this is not in the same place as the geographic North Pole. It is also slowly changing position over time, so in order to use a magnetic compass accurately, corrections must be made with the help of special charts.

**Compasses at sea**
Sailors need a reliable means of navigation to avoid being lost. Today some motor boats and canoes have adventure compasses (right) to show the way. Ships are built of metal, which can affect the readings of a magnetic compass, so a non-magnetic compass called a gyrocompass is used instead. Gyrocompasses are based on a device called a gyroscope (p. 73). The indicator in a gyrocompass always points to geographic North.

*Earth*

## LET'S EXPERIMENT
## MAKE A COMPASS

**YOU CAN MAKE A SIMPLE COMPASS,** like those used in ancient times, with ordinary materials from home. **You will need:** a large steel needle; a magnet with the poles marked; adhesive tape; a slice of cork; a container; water.

**1** To magnetize the needle, stroke a permanent magnet along it several times. To make the eye of the needle a north pole, you will need to stroke from the tip of the needle towards the eye with the south pole of the magnet. Be careful not to prick yourself with the point of the needle.

*The eye of the needle points north.*

**2** Tape the magnetized needle to the slice of cork, and float it in a container filled with water. The compass will swing round so that the eye of the needle is pointing towards geographical North.

# AURORAS

The Sun emits streams of charged particles into space, which can be attracted by the Earth's magnetic poles. The particles then interact with air molecules in the upper atmosphere to produce beautiful patterns of light known as auroras. The northern lights (*aurora borealis*) are the spectacular displays seen near the North Pole, while the lights at the South Pole are called the *aurora australis* (southern lights).

### Jupiter's magnetic field
The Earth is not the only planet to have a magnetic field. Jupiter has a magnetic field much stronger than Earth's. Neptune, Saturn, and Uranus also have stronger magnetic fields, while Mercury, Venus, and Mars all have weaker fields. Jupiter has auroras at its north and south poles that are 1,000 times brighter than Earth's auroras. They are thought to be produced by trapped particles from volcanic eruptions on Io, one of Jupiter's moons, as well as particles from the Sun.

*One of Jupiter's auroras photographed by the Hubble Space Telescope*

# MAGNETS

**ANY SUBSTANCE THAT CAN ATTRACT OR REPEL IRON**
is classed as a magnet. Other materials are also
attracted to magnets, and all these and iron are
known as magnetic materials. There are two types
of magnetic material, and both become magnetized
in a magnetic field. "Soft" magnetic materials, such
as nickel and iron, lose their magnetism when they
are removed from the field. "Hard" magnetic
materials, such as alloys of iron, nickel, cobalt,
and aluminium, become permanent
magnets once magnetized. Iron or steel
compass needles may be magnetized
by being stroked with a magnet.

## LODESTONES

Today most magnets are artificially made, but the first
compasses were made from the naturally occurring magnetic
mineral lodestone – now called magnetite. This lump of
magnetite (left) is attracting some iron filings. The word
magnet comes from Magnesia, a place in Turkey where magnetite
is found. It is believed that the ancient Chinese made the first
compass from magnetite in the 11th century, but the reason why
magnets point north was not understood until much later. In 1600,
the English scientist William Gilbert (1544–1603) explained that
the Earth acts like a giant magnet and attracts compass needles.

## MAGNETIC TYPES

We think of materials such as wood
that are not attracted to magnets as
non-magnetic. In fact all substances
are "diamagnetic", which means that
when they are exposed to a magnetic
field, they make their own field in
a way that makes them repel the
external field. Some substances are
also "paramagnetic", which is a much
stronger effect that covers up their
diamagnetism. Paramagnetic materials
are moderately attracted to magnetic
fields. Some paramagnetic materials
are also "ferromagnetic".
Ferromagnetic materials, such as
iron and nickel, are magnetized by
weak magnetic fields and are those
we normally think of as magnetic.
All magnetized materials produce
magnetic force fields around
themselves. These photographs
(right) show how iron filings can be
used to reveal magnetic force fields.

*The opposite poles of these magnets attract, and the
magnetic field between them is strengthened.*

*Like poles repel. There is a zero field point between them.*

**Unmagnetized material    Magnetized material**

### Magnetic domains

The atoms in magnetic materials are arranged
in groups, or domains, which behave like tiny
magnets. Normally these domains point in all
directions, cancelling out their magnetism.
However, in a magnetic field, the domains line
up in the same direction as the field, making
the material strongly magnetic. Hammering or
heating destroys the magnetization, by causing
the domains to point in all directions again.

**NORMALLY THE FORCE FIELD** around a magnet is invisible, but iron filings can reveal where it is. When they are brought near a magnet, the iron filings become magnets themselves with a north and south pole, and move to line up with the magnet's field. Wash your hands after touching iron filings. **You will need:** an adult's help; a permanent magnet; a large piece of paper; iron filings; a compass.

1 Place the magnet on the piece of paper. Ask an adult to sprinkle the iron filings carefully all over the paper around the magnet. Gently nudge the paper. The filings will line up along the magnetic field lines as shown.

2 A small compass can also be used to reveal the magnetic field as the compass needle lines up with the field lines. The stronger the magnetic field at any place, the closer together the field lines will be.

*The iron filings cluster near the poles, where the magnetic field is strongest.*

### Diamagnetic levitation

When living creatures, plants, plastic, and any other objects that are diamagnetic are placed in a magnetic field, all their atoms become slightly magnetic. Their electrons produce a weak magnetic field that opposes the field of the magnet they are near. This means that the atoms are repelled by the magnet. If this repelling force is as strong as the force of gravity that the object normally feels pulling it towards the ground, the object can be levitated above the magnet.

*The atoms in this frog are repelled by the magnet below it.*

*Disc drive motor*

### MiniDisc

Audio signals are stored in digital form on a magnetic layer inside a MiniDisc. When something is recorded, the playback laser heats the magnetic layer to about 180°C (356°F), while a magnetic recording head induces areas of north or south polarity. Areas left with a north pole represent digital "1"s, while those with a magnetic south pole represent "0"s. To play the recording, the laser beam operates at a lower power. Spots with south poles interact with the laser beam in a different way to those with north poles, which allows the data to be decoded and turned back into sound.

*Recording head*

# ELECTRIC CONNECTION

## MOST OF THE ELECTRIC MACHINES

in use today rely on electromagnets –
magnets whose power can be
switched on and off by an electric
current. The discovery in the
19th century of the connection
between electricity and magnetism,
known as electromagnetism, led to
the development of new machines for
a wide variety of tasks. Electromagnets
have many uses, ranging from lifting heavy
metal objects to providing propulsion in
levitating trains and allowing telephones
to work. Electromagnetism also forms the
basis for electric motors and generators.

*Horseshoe shaped
core of soft iron*

*Coiled
copper wire*

*Compass needle is
deflected by current.*

*Clamps hold the
current-carrying wire.*

*When the current is
switched off, the needle
points north.*

## ELECTROMAGNETISM

The link between electricity and magnetism was discovered
by the Danish physicist Hans Christian Oersted (1777–1851).
When he brought a compass near a current-carrying wire, the
needle moved. This showed that an electric current produces a
magnetic field. The French scientist André-Marie Ampère (1775–1836)
carried out further experiments and found that the strength of the
magnetic field around a wire increased as the current increased.

## ELECTROMAGNETS

In many electric devices a magnetic field
is only required some of the time. For
example, a doorbell uses an electromagnet
instead of a permanent magnet.
Electromagnets usually consist
of a coil of conducting wire around a
core of soft magnetic material such as
iron. When the electric current is
switched off, the magnet has no strength
(above). When a current flows through
the coil, the electromagnet is magnetized
(above right). If the direction of the
current changes, the north pole of the
electromagnet will become the south
pole and vice versa. The greater the
current flowing through the coil, and
the more wire it contains, the stronger
the electromagnet becomes.

*Iron filings*

### Maglev trains

Instead of running on rails, a maglev (magnetic
levitation) train uses electromagnetism to float above
the track. As magnets on the base of the carriages
pass conducting coils in the track, the coils become
temporary magnets. Their magnetic force repels
the magnets on the carriages, so the train floats.
The train moves because permanent
electromagnets in the track powered by
alternating current (pp. 140–141)
change polarity. The train is
attracted to the magnets ahead
and repelled by those behind it.

Connections to electric current

Coiled copper wire

Iron filings cling to the magnet.

## TELEPHONES

Electromagnets inside a telephone handset allow the caller to hear another person speaking. The mouthpiece contains a diaphragm that is vibrated by sound waves from a voice. These vibrations are converted into a varying electric current and sent down the telephone line. The signals can be heard because the receiver in the handset contains another diaphragm and an electromagnet. The variations in the current travelling down the telephone line vary the magnetic field that the electromagnet produces, making the diaphragm vibrate and reproduce the sound waves.

### Modems

It is not just conversations that can be transmitted by telephone lines. Computers can send e-mails and files to each other via a modem (above right). The modem converts binary information from a computer into tones, which are sent down telephone lines. The tones are then converted by another modem back into data. Most computers and some mobile phones have built-in modems.

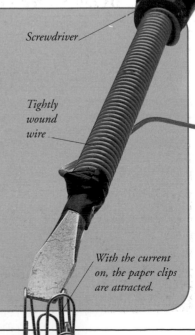

Screwdriver

Tightly wound wire

With the current on, the paper clips are attracted.

## LET'S EXPERIMENT
### MAKE AN ELECTROMAGNET

**YOU CAN MAKE** your own electromagnet that will lift small magnetic objects. Handle batteries with care and always follow instructions. **You will need:** an adult present; a screwdriver with a plastic handle; some copper wire; adhesive tape; a 9-volt battery; some paper clips.

**1** To turn the screwdriver into an electromagnet, first wind the copper wire tightly round the middle of it as shown (right). Use tape to secure the wire at each end.

**2** Connect one end of the wire to the positive terminal of the battery and the other end to the negative terminal. With both wires connected to the battery, the screwdriver becomes magnetized. Take care when handling the screwdriver as the copper wire may be hot.

**3** The screwdriver electromagnet can now be used to pick up paper clips and other objects made from magnetic materials. When the electromagnet is disconnected from the battery, it starts to lose its magnetism and drops whatever it is holding.

# GENERATING ELECTRICITY

## A CURRENT IS CREATED IN A CONDUCTING WIRE,

either when the wire moves past a magnetic field, or when a magnet moves past a stationary wire. This effect, called electromagnetic induction, was discovered independently by the American physicist Joseph Henry (1797–1878) in 1830 and the British scientist Michael Faraday (1791–1867) in 1831. Nearly all of the electricity we use today is created by electromagnetic induction, through enormous generators that turn mechanical energy into electrical energy.

*Thumb and two fingers all at right angles*

*1. Hold thumb upwards*

*2. First finger at right angle to thumb*

*3. Bend second finger at right angles to thumb and first finger*

**Fleming's right-hand rule**
Use your right hand to indicate the flow of an electric current when a wire moves through a magnetic field: thumb – direction of moving wire; first finger – direction of magnetic field; second finger – direction of induced current.

## GENERATORS

There are two types of generators. A dynamo produces direct current (DC), which flows in one direction all the time. An alternator produces alternating current (AC), which constantly changes direction. In both types of generator, the electric current is induced in a rotating coil of wire (armature) when it passes through a magnetic field. The electricity we use everyday is AC from alternators, while DC from dynamos is used for industrial electrolysis, such as electroplating and chemical manufacturing.

*An alternator*

*First half of the coil's turn*

*Current flows one way*

*South pole*

*South pole*

*Current flows the other way*

*North pole*

*Second half of the coil's turn*

**Dynamo**
As the wire coil rotates in a dynamo, one side passes the south pole of a permanent magnet, inducing a current in one direction. When the wire passes the north pole, a current flows in the opposite direction. A device called a commutator ensures that the current in the external circuit flows in only one direction.

**A dynamo**

*South pole*

*North pole*

*Armature*

*Commutator*

*External circuit*

**Alternator**
As the wire coil rotates in an alternator, current flows one way for half a turn as the coil passes one pole of the magnet. Current then flows in the opposite direction for the other half of the turn, as the coil passes the other magnetic pole. Power stations generate AC because it is easier to transmit over long distances.

## POWER STATIONS

Inside power stations are huge generators that are driven by the rotating shaft in an engine called a turbine. In coal and oil-fired power stations, heat from the burning fuel converts water into steam. The pressure of the steam rotates the turbine shaft. In nuclear power stations, the heat that converts water into steam comes from nuclear reactions, generally using uranium as fuel. Hydroelectric power stations use turbines driven by water rather than steam. Smaller amounts of electricity are being generated by solar power and wind power.

**A turbine and generator inside a nuclear power station**

# ELECTRICITY SUPPLY

A network of substations, overhead wires, and underground cables called a grid delivers electricity from power stations to homes and businesses. To be transmitted effectively, a higher voltage of electricity is needed. A lower voltage is needed for use at its destination. To increase and decrease the voltage, a transformer is used. Transformers have two separate coils of wire wound around an iron core. When alternating current (the type that constantly switches directions) flows through the primary coil, it creates an alternating magnetic field. This field induces an alternating electric current in the secondary coil. A step-up transformer has a secondary coil with more turns than the primary coil, increasing the voltage enough for transmission. A step-down transformer has a secondary coil with fewer turns, decreasing the voltage to a suitable level for use in homes and businesses.

*Primary coil*

*Secondary coil with more turns*

**Step-up transformer**

*Primary coil*

*Secondary coil with fewer turns*

**Step-down transformer**

### Electric fish
Some fish, such as electric eels and electric rays (above), have special muscle cells that generate and store electric currents. They produce strong electric shocks to stun or kill prey and as defence from predators. They also generate weaker electric pulses to help recognise prey and to navigate in murky water.

*Solar cell panels*

**Experimental solar-powered car**

### Solar energy
Sunlight can be converted into electricity in a device called a solar cell. Solar cells are made from two layers of silicon. Each layer has a different element added to it that alters its electrical properties. When sunlight falls on the surface of a solar cell, an electric current is generated across the junction between the layers. A small individual solar cell cannot produce much electricity, so many solar cells are usually connected together to form a solar panel. Solar panels are used to power electronic equipment in satellites and spacecraft. They are also used for home electricity generation and in experimental vehicles.

*Solar cells*

### Solar-powered wing
The *Helios* solar-powered flying wing was built as part of a NASA research project. It has a total wingspan of 75 m (247 ft), which is larger than the wingspan of a Boeing 747 aircraft. The pilot flies the *Helios* via remote control.

# MAKING MOTORS

**THE LINK BETWEEN ELECTRICITY AND MAGNETISM WAS** discovered when a compass needle swung round as it was brought near a wire carrying an electric current (p. 138). A year later, in 1821, British scientist Michael Faraday built the first electric motor, in which a wire carrying an electric current rotated around a fixed magnet. An electric motor is the opposite of an electric generator. In a generator, motion is used to create electricity, but in a motor, electricity is used to create motion.

*An electric current creates a magnetic field in the armature.*

*South pole*

*Battery provides electric current.*

*Magnetic poles either repel or attract the armature, making it spin.*

*North pole*

## ELECTRIC MOTORS

When an electric motor is switched on, a current flows through a coil of wire called an armature, which is located between the poles of a permanent magnet (above). The current creates a magnetic field in the armature with like poles in the armature facing like poles of the magnet. The like magnetic poles repel each other, pushing the armature around. As the armature turns, the poles approach the opposite poles of the magnet, and become attracted. The direction of the current is then reversed, and the poles on the armature switch over. As a result, the armature is repelled by the magnet again, and the rotation is complete. As long as there is an electric current, the armature spins between the poles of the magnet, creating motion. Electric motors range in size from relatively small, as in electrical appliances such as hairdryers, to very large, such as the motors used in electric trains.

**Disk drive**
This electric motor is from the floppy disk drive of a computer. An electric current causes small electromagnets on the turntable to generate a magnetic field that enables it to spin.

## ELECTRIC RAILWAYS

Most locomotives used to pull trains are powered by electric motors. An electric train receives the current needed to drive its motor either from an overhead cable or from a third rail on the track. To pick up the current from an overhead cable, a locomotive must have a flexible steel connector fitted to its roof. Many intercity trains use this system. To obtain the power from a third rail, a locomotive must have metal plates called shoes fitted underneath it, which make contact with the electrified rail. Local rail services often use this system. Trains on the London Underground in the UK (above) receive power from a third rail.

**TGV**
The large motors used in electric trains provide a lot of power, enabling trains to move very quickly. One of the fastest types of train is the TGV (Train à Grande Vitesse) in France (left), which can reach speeds of more than 300 kmh (180 mph). The TGV receives its power from overhead cables. Its streamlined shape allows it to speed along with a minimum of air resistance.

## Fleming's left-hand rule

Hold your left hand as shown to indicate which way a wire carrying an electric current moves through a magnetic field. The thumb shows the direction that the wire moves; the first finger, the direction of the magnetic field; the second finger, the direction of the electric current.

*Left-hand rule: thumb and two fingers all at right angles to each other (similar to right hand rule)*

*1. Hold thumb upwards.*

*2. Stretch first finger out, at right angle to thumb.*

*3. Bend second finger towards palm to form right angles with thumb and first finger.*

## Electric cars

It is possible for cars to be powered by electric motors, although electric cars are not common. In most types of electric car, a rechargeable battery provides an electric current to run the motor. Many electric cars cannot travel very fast, and their batteries frequently need recharging. Although electric cars themselves do not pollute, their batteries must be recharged using electricity from power stations, which may produce pollution. A more successful type of electric car, known as a hybrid (above), uses both electricity and another power source. The battery is partially recharged when braking.

# LET'S EXPERIMENT
## MAKE A MOTOR

**MAKE YOUR OWN** electric motor. Although it will not be very powerful, your motor will work in the same way as larger motors, and the armature (the moving part of the motor) should spin fairly quickly. Handle batteries with care and always follow instructions.
**You will need**: an adult present; about 1 m (3 ft 3 in) copper wire; cardboard tube (from toilet paper roll); small amount enamel or acrylic paint; two large paper clips; elastic bands; D cell battery (1.5 volt); bar magnet; glue.

*About seven loops in coil*

*Wrap ends of wire around sides of coil, leaving ends sticking straight out.*

**1** Use the copper wire to make the armature. Leaving about 6 cm (2 in) free at each end, wrap the wire around the cardboard tube. It should go around about seven times, with the two ends of the wire ending up on opposite sides of the coil (above). Slide the coil off the tube, then wrap the two free ends around the sides of the coil to hold it together.

*Paint top of wire end.*

**2** Paint the top half of one end of the wire using enamel or acrylic paint. Wait for it to dry. The paint is an electrical insulator, so once the motor is operating, it will break the electric circuit for half of each revolution.

*Bend paper clip at this point.*

**3** Bend two large paper clips in the middle (above). These will act as supports for the armature. Loop large elastic bands around the battery. Hook one paper clip to each end of the battery, using the elastic bands to keep the clips securely in place (below).

**4** Glue the bar magnet to the side of the battery. Hook the ends of the coil onto the paper-clip hooks and spin. If it does not work at first move the copper coil closer to the magnet or place it near a more powerful magnet.

*Magnet*

*One clip overlaps painted wire.*

*Spin the armature gently to help start it revolving.*

*Make sure paper clips are held securely to battery.*

*Paper clips support ends of coil.*

# ELECTRONICS AND CHIPS

**CRYSTAL WAFERS NOT MUCH BIGGER THAN YOUR** thumbnail are the "brains" behind computers and video games, mobile phones, and robots. They contain miniature components and circuits that control and manipulate flows of electrons. The study of electricity flowing through crystals, and also through gases or a vacuum, is known as electronics. The crystal wafers (chips), which have caused such a revolution in electronics in recent years, are made out of materials called semiconductors, or semimetals (pp. 46–47), which conduct electricity just a little.

In pure silicon, the atoms have four electrons, which are negatively charged, in their outer shells. Overall the atoms are electrically neutral.

An n-type semiconductor with a phosphorus atom, which has five outer electrons. This gives the material an extra electron and a negative charge.

## CLEVER CRYSTALS

Diodes and transistors are two of the most versatile components used in electronic circuits. They are both crystal devices, made up of semiconductor material. Diodes have two terminals and pass electric current only in one direction. Some give off light, and are called LEDs (light-emitting diodes). Transistors have three terminals – base, emitter, and collector. They can be used as switches (as in the experiment opposite) or as amplifiers, to amplify (strengthen) weak currents.

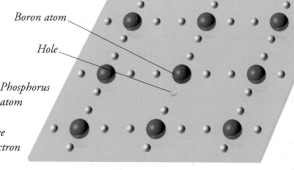

A p-type semiconductor with a boron atom, which has only three outer electrons. When boron replaces a silicon atom, there is one electron less, creating a positive hole.

## HOW SEMICONDUCTORS WORK

Elements like silicon and germanium become semiconductors when traces of certain impurities are introduced into them. Adding traces of boron to silicon creates a material with positively charged "holes". Under suitable conditions, these holes move around, allowing current to flow. This kind of semiconductor is called a *p* (positive)-type. Adding phosphorus or arsenic to silicon creates a material with spare electrons, which can flow to form a current. This is called an *n* (negative)-type semiconductor.

## INTEGRATED CIRCUITS

Electronic circuits were once made up of separate components, such as transistors and capacitors, linked together by wires. Now, most electronic devices have complete circuits in miniature, integrated in a single slice, or chip, of semiconductor material. They are called integrated circuits. The silicon chips used in the latest personal computers are made up of integrated circuits containing billions of components. Single chips can contain all the circuits that carry out processing in the computer (right), and are often called microprocessors or microchips.

**The crucial invention**
In 1947, a team of US scientists at Bell Laboratories in New Jersey, USA, made one of the crucial inventions of the 20th century. William Shockley, John Bardeen, and Walter Brattain developed the transistor. Their new device was much smaller, tougher, and consumed less power than the vacuum valves that it replaced in electronic circuits. In 1956 the men were jointly awarded the Nobel Prize for Physics.

# MAKING CHIPS

Silicon chips are produced hundreds at a time on a circular slice of pure silicon crystal. The circuits and different components (such as transistors and capacitors) are built up in a series of layers. Each layer is made by impregnating certain parts of the silicon with different elements, such as boron and phosphorus. When all the layers are complete, a layer of gold or aluminium is laid down to form the connections between the various components. Then the chips are inspected by probes and faulty ones are marked.

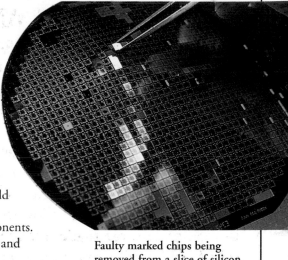

**Faulty marked chips being removed from a slice of silicon**

## LET'S EXPERIMENT
### MAKING A TRANSISTOR SWITCH

**YOU CAN USE A TRANSISTOR** as a switch to turn an LED (light-emitting diode) on and off. You do so by altering the connections to the transistor's base terminal. Handle batteries with care and always follow instructions. **You will need:** an adult's help; *n-p-n* transistor (BC108); an LED; 220 and 10,000 ohm resistors; battery pack (2 x 1.5-volts); electric leads with clips; insulated wire; short nails; eyelets; short lengths of wire; 2 wooden baseboards, soldering equipment; hammer.

**1** Attach the battery pack to a baseboard and connect lengths of wire to the battery terminals. Attach the other ends of the wires to the eyelets. Ask an adult to hammer nails into the other baseboard as shown (below). Connect up the circuit as shown in the photograph (right), wrapping the connecting wires of the components around the nails. Make sure that the transistor terminals – base, emitter, and collector – are the right way around.

**2** Ask an adult to solder the connecting wires to the nails and check that they are firm. Touch the end of the piece of insulated wire (the loose wire) to the middle nail on the negative side of the circuit, and the LED remains switched off. Touch it to the middle nail on the positive side, and the LED switches on.

*Wire from negative battery terminal*

*The wires from the terminals connect with the electric leads at the eyelets.*

*Wire from positive battery terminal*

*Insulated wire*

*Middle nail of negative side*

*Base*

*Emitter*

*Transistor*

*Collector*

*LED*

*Middle nail of positive side*

*10,000 ohm resistor*

*220 ohm resistor*

*Base (B) connected to negative terminal, collector (C) connected to positive terminal. LED stays off.*

*Base (B) and collector (C) both connected to positive terminal. Transistor switches on, lets current flow through LED.*

# ON THE RADIO

**WHIZZING ALL AROUND US AT THE SPEED OF** light are invisible waves carrying voices and music, messages and pictures, and even signals from outer space. They are radio waves, which are at the heart of most modern systems of communications. We pick up radio waves by tuning electronic circuits in our radios, televisions, and mobile phones. But what exactly are radio waves? They are tiny electrical and magnetic disturbances in space. These electromagnetic waves belong to the same family as light but have a much longer wavelength (up to several kilometres).

## PHONES ON THE MOVE

Using mobile phones, people can stay in touch with one another wherever they are by voice, text messaging, and, on WAP (wireless application protocol) phones, by e-mailing. Mobile phones work by radio waves. They send signals to an aerial up to a few kilometres away, which serves a small area called a cell. Signals picked up by the aerial are routed by computer via ordinary telephone links to a landline number, or to another mobile phone via the aerial of the cell in which it is located.

## CARRIER WAVES

How can sounds be sent through the air on radio waves? First, they are changed into electrical signals by a microphone. Then these signals are made to alter a radio wave, called the carrier wave, in a characteristic way. This process is called modulation. In amplitude modulation (AM), the voice signals are made to vary the amplitude of the carrier wave – the amount it vibrates up and down. In frequency modulation (FM), the voice signals vary the frequency of the carrier wave – the number of vibrations passing a certain point per second. FM transmissions suffer less from interference than AM.

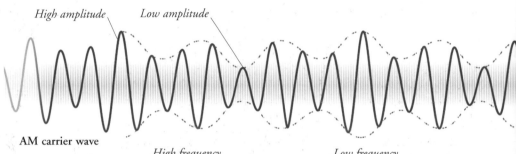

*High amplitude*  *Low amplitude*

**AM carrier wave**

*High frequency*  *Low frequency*

**FM carrier wave**

## LET'S EXPERIMENT
### MAKING RADIO WAVES

**MOST ELECTRICAL DEVICES** give out radio waves of some kind when they are switched on or off. The sudden surging or draining of current through their circuits disturbs the electrical and magnetic properties of the space around them.
**You will need:** a radio that has AM bands; torch.

**1** Switch on the radio and select an AM band. Bring the torch up close to the aerial and switch it on, then off. You should hear clicks on the radio.

**2** Tune the radio to different frequencies and repeat. Do the clicks get quieter or louder? What noise do you hear when you bring the radio near a television set?

SONY  TUNE

FM/υ  88 92 96 100 104 108  MHz
SCALE  0 1 2 3 4 5 6 7 8 9 10  ×100
AM/м  5.3  6  7 8  10 12 14 16  kHz
FM  AM

# RADAR WAVES

Aircraft and ships use radio waves not only for
communications, but also for navigation. They use radar
to see the traffic around them. The word radar stands for
radio detection and ranging. Radar sets transmit pulses
of radio waves and pick up any echoes when the beams
are reflected from nearby objects. The reflections are
displayed on a screen. The time it takes for the echoes
to return gives the range (distance away) of the objects.

**Radar
screen
showing objects
surrounding a ship (centre).**

*Scanning coil sweeps
beams back and forth
across the screen.*

*Shadow mask allows each
beam to strike the appropriate
coloured phosphor.*

*Phosphor stripes will glow
red, blue, or green when
electron beams hit them.*

*Anode and cathode
(inside tube)*

*Three
electron guns
(not visible) here
produce beams representing red,
green, and blue colours in the picture.*

**Inside a television set**

# AS SEEN ON TV

Radio waves carry television picture signals to a
receiver, which converts them into images. The
key device in the receiver is the cathode-ray tube
(CRT). Electronic circuits sort out the incoming
signals into four main sets: three representing the
colours red, green, and blue in the picture being
transmitted, and one set of scanning signals. The
colour signals are fed to electron guns, which fire
beams of electrons at the screen, where they strike
phosphors (p. 120) that glow with the appropriate
colour. The scanning signals make the beams scan
across the screen. This happens so quickly that
our eyes see a full-screen picture.

## ◂ TUNING IN ▸

In 1932, a US electrical engineer
named Karl Jansky detected radio
waves coming from space, and
launched radio astronomy.
Astronomers pick up radio waves from
space with huge, dish-shaped radio
telescopes. Their study of the radio
universe led to the discovery of new
astronomical bodies, such as quasars,
pulsars, and radio galaxies. **113** ▸

*Parkes radio telescope in New South Wales,
Australia, has a dish 64 m (210 ft) across.*

# COMPUTING

**WHEN THE SPACE SHUTTLE BLASTS OFF THE** launch pad, 300,000 operations must be performed every second to ensure that all its systems function properly. Human astronauts could not possibly cope with such demands, which is why lift-off is controlled by computers. Within their electronic circuits, computers are capable of carrying out millions of operations every second. Exactly what a computer does depends on the way it is programmed (instructed). It may be used to play games, design the molecules of new drugs, pilot airliners, write novels, or create imaginary, virtual worlds.

*Screen*

*Keyboard*

## HARDWARE

The pieces of equipment that make up a computer are called the hardware. The key component is the CPU (central processing unit), the computer's main control unit. Other chips hold the computer's memories, the permanent ROM (read-only memory), and temporary RAM (random-access memory). Information is fed into the computer by keyboard, mouse, and from storage discs, usually magnetic CDs (compact discs) or DVDs (digital versatile discs). Information and graphics (pictures) are displayed on a screen, and may be printed out as "hard copy".

*Car designed with a program called CAD (computer-assisted design), which uses advanced 3-D graphics*

## SOFTWARE

The programs and data (information) fed into a computer are called the software. Before it can be handled by the computer, software has to be translated into binary code, in which information is represented by the two digits 1 and 0. These digits can then be represented in the computer's electronic circuits by the flow (1) or non-flow (0) of electricity. (This is achieved by switching electric current on and off with transistors.) Each 1 or 0 is called a bit; a set of eight bits is called a byte. Computer programmers write their programs in "computer language", such as BASIC or COBOL, which the computer can recognize and translate into binary code (machine code).

**Like the real thing**
A pilot "flies" a fighter in a computer-generated landscape (left). The plane responds to the pilot's actions just like a real plane would. The ultimate in this kind of computer simulation is virtual reality, in which you can enter a virtual (created) world that the computer produces. You wear a helmet that shows the virtual world on screens before your eyes. You can "touch" virtual objects using a glove wired-up with sensors.

## SURFING THE NET

Through your computer, you can join a worldwide computer network known as the Internet, which you can tap into via the telephone. The "Net" allows access to an almost unlimited amount of information on every subject you can think of. It also lets you communicate with other computer users by electronic mail (e-mail). On the Net, companies, universities, shops, special interest groups, and individuals provide information through different websites. From them, you can download (put onto your computer) text, graphics, photographs, and even video footage and music. Search engines provide a quick way of looking for the information you want.

## ROBOTS AT WORK

An inspection robot pilots itself through a sewer pipe, using twin laser beams to guide itself (left). Most industrial robots look nothing like the androids (artificial humans), depicted in comics and films. They are built to be functional – to do a specific job in the best possible way. In industry, robots are widely used on car assembly lines for welding and paint spraying. Unlike humans, they can carry on doing these messy, repetitive jobs indefinitely without tiring or getting fed up!

*Four cameras in the head help Dynamic Brain pinpoint the beanbag's exact position.*

### Artificial intelligence

A robot called "Dynamic Brain" juggles with beanbags (right). Machines like this are being developed in research on artificial intelligence (AI). The aim of AI is to create devices that can learn by experience and make decisions, without being programmed to do so each time. In one line of research, scientists are developing neural networks that try to imitate the way the brain works.

# GLOSSARY

**Absolute zero:** lowest temperature possible, when all molecular motion ceases, 0K or -273.15°C (-460°F)

**Absorption:** (1) In physics, taking in of energy (e.g. heat, light, sound) by a substance. (2) In chemistry, the take-up of a gas by a liquid or solid, or of a liquid by a solid.

**Acceleration:** rate of change of velocity, expressed in units such as metres per second per second.

**Acid:** compound containing hydrogen that splits up in water to produce positive hydrogen ions.

**Acid rain:** rain containing acids produced in the air from polluting gases, such as sulphur dioxide.

**Acoustics:** study of sound. The sound properties of a building are called its acoustics.

**Adhesion:** attraction between the atoms or molecules of different substances.

**Aerodynamics:** study of gases (particularly air) in motion and of objects moving through them.

**Aerofoil:** wing-shape that cuts through the air, creating lift.

**Air resistance:** *See Drag.*

**Alchemy:** early chemical science in which people (alchemists) investigated chemicals and reactions in an effort to make, for example, gold from base metals.

**Alkali:** base that dissolves in water.

**Allotropes:** different forms of the same element, e.g. oxygen and ozone.

**Alloy:** mixture of two or more metals, or of a metal and a non-metal.

**Alpha rays:** stream of particles given off by radioactive substances, consisting of the nuclei of helium atoms.

**Alternating current (AC):** electric current that flows first in one direction, then in another, at a constant frequency. Mains electricity is AC.

**Alternator:** electric generator that produces alternating current.

**Ammeter:** instrument that measures electric current.

**Ampere (amp):** unit of electric current.

**Amplifier:** device that magnifies or strengthens electrical signals.

**Amplitude:** maximum height plus depth of a wave.

**Angular momentum:** momentum possessed by a rotating object.

**Anion:** negatively charged ion that moves to the anode during electrolysis.

**Anode:** positive electrode.

**Antimatter:** matter made up of particles that are exact opposites of the ones in ordinary matter. Positrons (positively charged) are the antiparticles of electrons (negatively charged).

*Red cabbage can be used as an indicator to test the level of* **acid** *in a substance.*

**Artificial element:** element produced artificially by nuclear bombardment.

**Atmospheric pressure:** pressure of the air in the atmosphere, about 100 kilopascals or 1 kg per square centimetre (14.7 pounds per square inch) at sea level.

**Atom:** smallest particle of an element that can exist and still have the properties of that element.

**Atomic energy:** *See Nuclear energy.*

**Atomic number:** number of protons in the nucleus of an atom.

**Atomic weight:** *See Relative atomic mass.*

**Barometer:** instrument that measures air pressure.

**Base:** in chemistry, a compound that reacts with an acid to produce a salt and water only.

**Battery:** series of electric cells joined together to produce and store electricity.

**Beta rays:** streams of electrons given off by radioactive substances.

**Binary number:** number system based on two digits, 0 and 1.

**Biochemistry:** study of the chemical reactions that take place in living organisms.

**Biology:** study of living things, comprising two main branches – botany, the study of plants and zoology, the study of animals.

**Bioluminescence:** light without heat produced by living organisms (such as glow-worms).

**Black hole:** a region of space with such intense gravity that nothing can escape it, not even light.

**Boiling point:** temperature at which a liquid bubbles and changes into gas.

**Bonds:** attractions between atoms or ions that hold molecules and other compounds together. *See also Covalent, Ionic, and Metallic bond.*

**Bubble chamber:** device for detecting charged atomic particles. The particles leave a trail of bubbles behind when they pass through it.

**Buoyancy:** upward force exerted on a body immersed in a fluid.

**Burning:** *See Combustion.*

**Capacitor:** device in electronic circuits that stores electric charge.

**Cathode:** negative electrode.

**Cathode-ray tube (CRT):** vacuum tube in which a stream of electrons (cathode rays) makes phosphors on a screen fluoresce, or give out light.

**Cation:** positively charged ion that moves to the cathode during electrolysis.

**Cell:** (1) in biology, the basic unit from which all organisms are made up. (2) In electricity, a device that produces electricity through chemical changes. *See also Battery.*

**Celsius:** temperature scale devised by Anders Celsius (1701–44), on which water freezes at 0 degrees.

**Central processing unit (CPU):** principal part of a computer, which carries out the processing of data.

**Centre of gravity (or mass):** point in a body in which all its weight (or mass) seems to be concentrated.

**Centripetal force:** force in rotating bodies which acts inwards to keep them turning in a circle.

*The circulating streams of rising and descending air that enable this glider to fly are known as* **convection** *currents.*

**Capillary action:** movement of a liquid up or down a narrow tube because of attraction between its molecules and those of the tube.

**Carbohydrate:** energy-giving compound made up of carbon, hydrogen, and oxygen.

**Carbon chemistry:** *See Organic chemistry.*

**Carrier waves:** radio waves that carry signals, as in radio and TV.

**Catalyst:** substance that speeds up a chemical reaction without itself undergoing chemical change.

**Chain reaction:** reaction that continues on its own. In a nuclear chain reaction, particles produced when one atom splits (undergoes fission) trigger more atoms to split.

**Charge (or electric charge):** a property of many subatomic particles that makes them attract or repel one another. It takes two forms – negative and positive. The electron has a single negative charge, a proton a single positive charge.

**Chemical reaction:** process in which substances (reactants) undergo chemical change and form new substances (products).

**Chemistry:** study of the properties and make-up of substances and the changes they undergo.

**Chromatography:** method of separating substances in a mixture by passing it through a medium (such as filter paper). The

Concave lens

Convex lens

*Concave lenses cause light rays to diverge (spread out), whereas **convex** lenses cause light rays to converge (come together).*

substances separate because they flow through at different speeds.

**Circuit:** path through which an electric current can flow. *See also Integrated circuit.*

**Cohesion:** force of attraction between particles of the same substance.

**Combustion (or burning):** chemical reaction in which substances combine with oxygen in the air to produce heat (and usually light as flames).

**Composite:** material made of different substances, such as plastic reinforced with fibres.

**Compound:** substance formed by the combination of two or more different elements in fixed proportions.

**Concave lens:** lens that curves inwards, like a dish.

**Condensation:** change of state from a gas (or vapour) into a liquid.

**Conduction:** process in which heat, sound, or electricity passes through a substance.

**Conductor:** substance that passes heat, sound, or electricity well.

**Conservation of energy:** energy cannot be created or destroyed, merely changed from one form to another.

**Contraction:** shrinking in size, as when a hot body cools.

**Convection:** transfer of heat through a liquid or a gas by moving currents.

**Convex lens:** lens that curves outwards, bulging in the middle.

**Corrosion:** chemical or electrochemical attack on a metal surface. *See also Rusting.*

**Covalent bond:** bond formed when atoms share pairs of electrons with one another.

**Cracking:** oil refining process in which catalysts are used to help break down heavy oil fractions into lighter, more useful products.

**Cryogenics:** study of materials at very low temperatures, such as liquid gases.

**Crystal:** solid substance with a regular shape due to the internal arrangement of its particles. *See also Lattice.*

**Data:** information.

**Decibel:** unit used to measure the intensity (loudness) of sound.

**Deliquescence:** absorption of moisture from the atmosphere by a substance to the point that it eventually dissolves.

**Density:** mass of a certain volume of a substance (such as kilograms per cubic metre). *See also Relative density.*

**Deoxyribonucleic acid (DNA):** chemical that makes up the chromosomes in the cells of living things. It forms the genes that pass on characteristics from one generation to another.

**Detergent:** chemical that helps dirt and grease dissolve in water; used for cleaning.

**Diffraction:** spreading out of waves when they pass through a thin slit.

**Diffusion:** mixing of different substances as a result of the movement of their particles.

**Diode:** crystal semiconductor device that passes current only one way. *See also Light emitting diode.*

**Direct current (DC):** electric current that flows in only one direction through a circuit.

**Distillation:** process for purifying or separating liquids. The liquid (or liquid mixture) is boiled into vapour, which is then condensed.

**Drag:** force of resistance an object experiences when it travels through a fluid (gas or liquid), caused by friction with the surrounding molecules.

**Dynamo:** electric generator that produces direct current.

**Echo:** sound heard again after it has been reflected from an object.

**Echolocation:** method of detection and navigation using echoes, used in nature by bats and dolphins. Radar and sonar employ the same principles.

**Eclipse:** shadow cast by the Moon on the Earth when the Moon passes in front of the Sun, or by the Earth on the Moon.

**Effort:** force needed to move a load.

**Elasticity:** property of a material allowing it to return to its original size after it has been stretched.

**Electric current:** flow of electrons or ions in a circuit.

**Electricity:** effects resulting from the movement of electric charges (in current electricity) or from stationary charges (in static electricity).

**Electrochemistry:** study of the chemistry involved with ions in solution, as in electric cells and electrolysis.

**Electrode:** conductor that emits or collects electrons in a cell, semiconductor, or circuit.

**Electrolysis:** production of a chemical reaction by passing an electric current through an electrolyte.

**Electrolyte:** liquid that conducts electricity, as in electrolysis.

**Electromagnetic radiation:** waves of energy that are tiny electric and magnetic disturbances in space.

**Electromagnetic spectrum:** family of electromagnetic waves,

which differ in their wavelength. They range from the shortest-wave (or highest-frequency) gamma rays to the longest-wave (lowest-frequency) radio waves.

**Electromotive force (emf):** driving force of a cell or generator, which "pushes" the electrons around a circuit. *See also Potential difference.*

**Electron:** one of the three main particles in an atom (with the proton and neutron). It carries a negative charge. Electric current is a flow of electrons.

**Electron gun:** device that produces electrons in a cathode-ray tube and "shoots" them at the screen.

**Electronics:** study of the flow of electrons in semiconductor crystals, gases, and a vacuum, and the design of devices that rely on such flow. *See also Integrated circuit, Semiconductor.*

**Electron microscope:** microscope that uses electron beams in order to produce magnified images.

**Electroplating:** coating one metal with another by means of electrolysis.

**Electroscope:** device for detecting electric charge.

**Electrostatics:** study of electric charges at rest and the force fields around them.

**Element:** substance that cannot be broken down into simpler substances. There are about 90 naturally occurring elements and 19 artificial ones.

**Elementary particles:** *See Fundamental particles.*

**Emulsion:** tiny particles of one liquid dispersed (scattered) in another.

*This toy – a slinky – has **elasticity**, which allows it to return to its original shape after it has been stretched.*

**Endothermic reaction:** chemical reaction in which heat is taken in. *Compare Exothermic reaction.*

151

**Energy:** ability to do work. *See also Conservation of energy.*

**Enzyme:** protein that acts as a catalyst in the chemical reactions that take place in living things.

**Equation:** in chemistry, a shorthand method of representing a chemical reaction, using symbols to represent the elements involved, as in the burning of hydrogen: $2H_2 + O_2 = 2H_2O$.

**Equilibrium:** balanced state; for example, a lever is in equilibrium when the effort balances the load.

**Evaporation:** change of state in which a liquid changes into a gas (or vapour). It can take place at any temperature above the liquid's freezing point.

**Exothermic reaction:** chemical reaction in which heat is given out. *Compare Endothermic reaction.*

**Expansion:** increasing in size, as when a body gets hotter.

**Fahrenheit scale:** temperature scale named after Gabriel Fahrenheit (1686–1736), on which water freezes at 32 degrees. *See also Celsius scale, Kelvin scale.*

**Fermentation:** common chemical reaction in which yeast converts sugars into alcohol, with carbon dioxide being given off.

**Fibre optics:** *See Optical fibres.*

**Field:** region in which a body experiences a force. Fields exist around magnets (magnetic field), charges (electric fields), and massive bodies because of their gravity (gravitational field).

**Fission:** *See Nuclear fission.*

**Floppy disc:** flexible plastic disc with a magnetic coating, used to store data and programs in computing.

**Fluid:** substance that flows – a liquid or gas.

**Fluorescence:** visible light given off by some substances when they absorb ultraviolet radiation.

**Focus:** point at which light rays converge after passing through a lens or after reflection by a mirror.

**Force:** something that changes the speed, direction, or shape of a body.

**Force field:** *See Field.*

**Formula:** set of chemical symbols that represents the composition of a substance, as in $CaCO_3$, which is calcium carbonate or chalk.

**Fossil:** remains of a once living organism.

**Fossil fuel:** coal, oil, or natural gas, which are the remains of organisms that lived hundreds of millions of years ago.

**Freezing point:** temperature at which a liquid changes into a solid.

**Frequency:** of a wave form, the number of complete waves passing a certain point each second; measured in hertz (Hz).

**Frequency modulation (FM):** method of changing (modulating) the frequency of a radio wave to carry signals.

**Friction:** force that resists the movement of one surface over another.

**Fuel cell:** electric cell in which electricity is produced directly from a fuel. The space shuttle uses fuel cells in which hydrogen reacts with oxygen to produce water.

**Fulcrum:** point at which a lever pivots.

**Fundamental forces:** four main forces of the Universe, which are gravity, electromagnetic force, strong force, and weak force. The last two act only at very short distances within the nucleus of atoms.

**Fuse:** safety device in an electric circuit that breaks the circuit if the current rises too high.

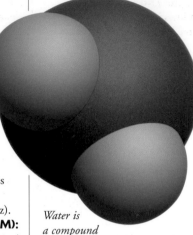

*Water is a compound of two atoms of **hydrogen** and one of atom of oxygen.*

**Galvanized:** coated with a thin layer of zinc, to protect metals such as iron or steel from rust.

**Galvanometer:** instrument for detecting and measuring small electric currents.

**Gamma rays:** electromagnetic rays of very short wavelength that are emitted by certain radioactive substances.

**Gas:** state of matter in which the particles are far apart and move about randomly and quickly.

**Generator:** machine that converts mechanical energy into electricity. *See also Alternator, Dynamo.*

**Geothermal energy:** heat tapped from rocks deep in the Earth's crust.

**Global warming:** increase in the world's atmospheric temperature, probably caused by an increased greenhouse effect.

**Gluons:** particles within protons and neutrons that hold the quarks in place.

**Gravity:** force of attraction between any two bodies. It is the Earth's gravity that keeps our feet on the ground and makes objects fall when we drop them. Gravity is one of the fundamental forces of the Universe. *See also Fundamental forces.*

**Greenhouse effect:** build-up of certain gases in the atmosphere (such as carbon dioxide) that is causing the atmosphere to behave like a greenhouse, trapping heat

*Gyroscope resists having its direction of movement changed because of **inertia**.*

from the Sun.

**Grid:** network of transmission lines by which electricity is distributed around the country.

**Group:** vertical column in the Periodic Table containing elements with similar chemical properties. *See also Periodic Table.*

**Gyroscope:** fast-rotating wheel, which resists disturbance because of its angular momentum. Once set spinning, its axis always keeps pointing in the same direction, a property used in the gyrocompass.

**Halogen:** group VII in the Periodic Table containing reactive elements like fluorine and chlorine.

**Hardware:** pieces of equipment that make up a computer system.

**Heat:** a form of energy transferable from one body or system to another because of a difference in temperature.

**Heat engine:** machine for converting heat energy into work, such as a steam or petrol engine.

**Heat transfer:** movement of heat from a hotter to a colder body, by conduction, convection, or radiation.

**Holography:** method of producing a three-dimensional image using laser light.

**Humidity:** amount of water vapour in the atmosphere.

**Hydraulics:** study of fluids at rest and in motion, particularly in regard to the design of machines that work by fluid pressure.

**Hydrocarbon:** compound containing hydrogen and carbon only; oil and natural gas are made up mainly of hydrocarbons.

**Hydrodynamics:** study of fluids in motion.

**Hydroelectric power:** electricity produced by harnessing the energy in flowing water.

**Hydrogen:** simplest and most abundant element in the Universe. It has two allotropes, deuterium and tritium.

**Hydrometer:** device for measuring the density of a liquid.

**Hydrostatics:** study of liquids at rest.

**Immiscible:** term that describes two liquids that do not mix, such as oil and water.

**Imperial units:** units still used in some English-speaking countries, including the pound, inch, foot and mile. *See also SI units.*

**Indicator:** substance used to show (indicate) the pH (acidity or alkalinity) of a solution by its colour.

**Inert gases:** *See Noble gases.*

**Inertia:** property of a body that makes it resist any change in motion. Mass is a measure of inertia.

**Infrared rays (IR):** invisible electromagnetic radiation with a wavelength longer than red light; produced by hot bodies.

**Infrasound:** sound waves with too low a frequency to be detected by the human ear.

**Inorganic chemistry:** the study of compounds that are not carbon-based.

**Insulator:** material that is a poor conductor of heat, electricity, or sound.

**Integrated circuit:** miniature electronic circuit in which all the components (e.g. capacitors, resistors, transistors) are integrated (contained) in one piece of semiconductor.

**Interference:** disturbance produced when two or more waves (e.g. light, sound) interact.

**Internal combustion engine:** engine in which fuel is burned inside the engine.

**Ion:** atom or group of atoms that has lost or gained one or more electrons to become electrically charged. *See also Anion, Cation.*

**Ionic bond:** bond formed between positive and negative ions, formed when one or more electrons is transferred from one atom to another.

**Isotopes:** atoms of the same element with the same number of protons in the nucleus, but with different numbers of neutrons.

**Jet propulsion:** propulsion of a body by a jet of gas or liquid. The action (force) of the jet moving backwards produces a reaction (force in the opposite direction) that propels the body forwards.

**Joule:** unit of energy and work in the SI system.

*Iron filings reveal the* **magnetic field** *around a magnet.*

**Kelvin:** unit of temperature in the SI system, widely used in science. Named after physicist Lord Kelvin (1824–1907), it begins at absolute zero, which is 0 kelvin (K). The freezing point of water is about 273 K.

**Kilogram:** unit of mass in the SI system.

**Kinetic energy:** energy a body has because of its motion.

**Kinetic theory:** *See Particle theory.*

**Laser:** device that produces an intense beam of pure light (of a single wavelength). Laser stands for light amplification by the stimulated emission of radiation.

**Latent heat:** heat that is taken in or given out when a substance changes state.

*The fat and fur of a polar bear are poor conductors of heat, therefore they are good* **insulators** *– the heat built up in the bear's body cannot travel well and escape easily.*

**Lattice:** regular arrangement of the particles (e.g. atoms, ions) in a crystal.

**Lens:** curved piece of glass or other transparent material that brings light rays to a focus. *See also Concave lens, Convex lens.*

**Lepton:** class of fundamental particle that includes the electron.

**Lever:** simple machine consisting of a rigid beam, turning around a pivot, or fulcrum. A force (effort) is applied at one point to lift a force (load) at another.

**Lift:** upward force produced on a wing or aerofoil when it moves through the air.

**Light:** electromagnetic radiation that our eyes can detect. White light is a mixture of all the colours of the rainbow, which form the visible spectrum.

**Light-emitting diode (LED):** Crystal diode that gives off light when electric current passes through it.

**Light year:** distance light travels in a year which is about 9.5 million million km (5.9 million million miles).

**Liquid:** state of matter between a solid and a gas, in which the particles move about in bundles but are still quite close together and attract one another.

**Liquid crystal:** substance that flows like a liquid but has its particles arranged in an ordered structure, like a crystal.

**Liquid crystal display (LCD):** Sets of liquid crystals that, in an electric field, can twist light passing through them to produce dark segments that can make digits (numbers), for example.

**Litmus:** common indicator that turns red in acid solutions, blue in alkaline.

**Longitudinal wave:** wave in which vibrating particles vibrate in the direction in which the wave is travelling. Sound is a longitudinal wave.

**Loudness:** intensity of sound, measured in decibels.

**Lunar eclipse:** eclipse of the Moon, when it passes into the Earth's shadow in space.

**Magnetic field:** field of force that exists around a magnetic body.

**Magnetism:** property of some materials, especially iron, to attract or repel like materials.

**Mass:** amount of matter in a body; a measure of the body's inertia. *Compare Weight.*

**Matter:** anything that has mass and occupies space.

**Mechanical advantage:** measure of the effectiveness of a machine to magnify effort to move greater loads.

**Melting point:** temperature at which a solid turns into a liquid.

**Meniscus:** curved upper surface of a liquid in a tube.

**Metal:** element that conducts heat and electricity well and is usually solid, hard, and shiny.

**Metallic bond:** bond in metals in which the electrons can flow freely between the atoms.

**Microchip:** silicon chip that carries miniaturized electronic circuits.

**Microgravity:** condition experienced in an orbiting spacecraft, where gravity is reduced to about one ten-thousandth of its value at the Earth's surface. Also called zero-g or weightlessness.

**Microscope:** instrument with lenses that produces an enlarged image of an object. *See also Electron microscope.*

**Microwaves:** electromagnetic waves with wavelengths between infrared rays and radio waves.

**Mineral:** naturally occurring inorganic substances; the main constituents of rocks.

**Mixture:** substance that contains two or more different elements or compounds mixed together but not combined chemically. *Contrast Compound.*

**Molecule:** smallest unit of an element or compound which is made of two or more atoms bonded together.

**Momentum:** tendency of a body to keep on moving, measured by its mass times its velocity.

**Monomer:** small molecule that is the basic building block of a polymer.

**Neutralization:** reaction in which an acid reacts with a base to produce a salt and water.

**Neutrino:** subatomic particle that has neither mass nor charge, only spin energy; one kind of lepton.

**Neutron:** particle found in the nuclei of all atoms except hydrogen. It has a similar mass to the proton but no electric charge.

**Newton (N):** unit of force in the SI system.

**Noble gases:** gaseous elements that don't react easily with other elements. Once called rare gases and inert gases.

**Non-metals:** elements that don't behave like metals and are typically poor conductors of heat and electricity. They include solids like sulphur and gases like chlorine.

**Nuclear energy:** energy released when the nucleus of an atom is split (fission) or joined to another (fusion).

**Nuclear fission:** nuclear reaction in which the nuclei of heavy atoms split, releasing energy.

**Nuclear fusion:** nuclear reaction in which the nuclei of light atoms join together, releasing energy.

**Nuclear reactor:** device in which a nuclear reaction can be controlled to produce a steady flow of energy.

**Nucleus:** centre part of an atom, made up of protons and neutrons. It contains most of the atom's mass and has a positive charge.

**Optical fibres:** fine glass or plastic fibres that transmit light by total internal reflection.

**Orbit:** path of one body around another.

**Ore:** mineral from which a metal can be extracted; often profitably.

**Organic chemistry:** chemistry of the carbon compounds, some found in living things.

**Organism:** living thing, made up of one or more cells.

**Oxidation:** chemical reaction in which a substance combines with oxygen. Combustion and rusting are common examples of oxidation. *See also Reduction.*

**Particles:** basic units from which all substances are made up, such as atoms and molecules. Subatomic particles are particles smaller than an atom, such as protons.

**Particle accelerator:** machine that accelerates beams of charged particles (protons, electrons) to high energies. Also called an atom-smasher.

**Particle theory:** theory that all matter is composed of particles in constant motion. The way they interact explains the three states of matter – solids, liquids, and gases – and the way they change from one to the other. Also known as kinetic theory.

**Periodic Table:** table in which all the elements are listed in order of atomic number and arranged so that elements with similar properties fall together.

**Petrochemicals:** chemicals produced from petroleum at an oil refinery, by processes like distillation and cracking.

**pH:** measure of how acidic or how alkaline a solution is. pH 0 or 1 is highly acid, pH 14 is highly alkaline.

**Photon:** particle that is the smallest unit of electromagnetic radiation, consisting of a single quantum of energy.

**Photosynthesis:** process by which plants make food in their leaves, using the energy in sunlight. They combine carbon dioxide (which they take in from the air) with water (which they take in with their roots) to make sugars.

**Physics:** study of energy and forces. Nuclear physics, for example, studies the energy and forces within the nuclei of atoms.

**Plasma:** state of matter that exists at very high temperatures (like in stars) in which the atoms are separated into electrons and ions.

**Plastic:** synthetic product consisting of long-chain molecules, or polymers. Thermoplastics (like nylon) soften when heated, but thermosets (like Bakelite) remain rigid.

**Polarized light:** light whose waves vibrate in only one plane. Ordinary light waves vibrate in all planes.

**Pollution:** poisoning of the environment (air, water, and land) by substances such as oil, chemicals, and nuclear waste.

**Polymers:** substances with long chains of atoms, made up of repeated units. Plastics are synthetic polymers made by polymerization, a chemical process that combines small molecules (monomers) to form big ones (polymers).

**Potential difference:** difference in electrical energy between two points in an electric circuit. It provides the driving force for electric current. Measured in volts.

**Potential energy:** energy stored for later use. Gravitational potential energy is the energy stored in a body because of its position, such as a roller-coaster.

**Pressure:** force acting against a certain area, usually measured in pascals (newtons per square metre).

**Primary colours:** colours from which all other colours can be produced. In light, the primary colours are red, green, and blue. In paints and pigments, the primary colours are yellow, magenta (reddish-blue), and cyan (bluish-green).

**Prism:** triangular wedge of glass or other transparent material that can split up white light into a spectrum of colours.

**Program:** set of instructions to make a computer perform certain operations.

**Proton:** one of the two main particles found in the nucleus of atoms. It has the same mass as the neutron, but has a positive charge.

**Quantum:** a tiny "packet" of energy. Electromagnetic radiation is thought of as a stream of quanta (the plural of quantum) known as photons.

**Quantum mechanics:** science explaining the properties and behaviour of atoms and molecules, based on the idea that energy is emitted in quanta.

**Quarks:** fundamental particles from which protons and neutrons are made up.

**Radar (radio detection and ranging):** detection of objects by bouncing radio beams off them and listening for the echoes.

**Radiation:** energy travelling as electromagnetic waves (such as light). Also, the rays given off by radioactive substances, such as alpha, beta, and gamma rays.

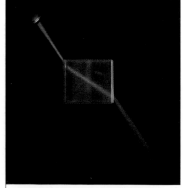

*Refraction occurs when a beam of light is passed through a glass block. The light beam bends as it moves from air to glass.*

**Radioactivity:** breakdown of the nucleus of certain elements, causing radiation to be given off.

*The **surface tension** of the milk is broken as detergent is dripped onto it.*

**Random-access memory (RAM):** temporary memory in a computer, in which data can be stored and retrieved.

**Reactants:** substances that take part in a chemical reaction.

**Read-only memory (ROM):** permanent memory in a computer, which cannot be altered.

**Reduction:** reaction in which a substance loses oxygen or, more broadly, gains electrons. The opposite of oxidation.

**Reflection:** bouncing back of a wave (such as light) from a surface.

**Refraction:** bending of a beam of light as it passes from one medium to another (such as air to water).

**Relative atomic mass:** means of comparing the masses of atoms. It is the ratio of the mass of an atom to one-twelfth of the mass of the carbon-12 atom. Formerly called atomic weight.

**Relative density:** density of a substance compared with the density of a reference substance, usually water.

**Resistance:** in electrical circuits, the property that opposes the flow of electricity. Resistors are components that have a known resistance.

**Rusting:** process by which iron and steel combine with the oxygen in the air to form iron oxide. Rusting is the commonest form of corrosion.

**Salt:** substance formed when an acid reacts with a base or a metal.

**Scalar quantity:** quantity that just has magnitude, such as temperature.

**Semiconductor:** crystalline solid that can conduct small amounts of electric current under suitable conditions. Semiconductors (such as silicon) are the basis of modern integrated electronic circuits.

**Semimetal:** element that has properties between those of a metal and those of a non-metal. Including boron, silicon, germanium, and arsenic, they are useful as semiconductors.

**Shock wave:** high-pressure wave set up when air compresses then expands very rapidly and when an object travels supersonically (faster than the speed of sound) through the air.

**SI units:** system of standard measuring units used in science. SI stands for *Système International d'Unités*. It has replaced the former Imperial and c.g.s. (centimetre-gram-second) units.

**Software:** programs and data fed into a computer. *Compare Hardware.*

**Solar cell:** electric cell that converts the energy in sunlight directly into electricity.

**Solute:** substance that dissolves in a liquid to form a solution.

**Solution:** special kind of mixture in which a gas, solid, or liquid is dissolved in a liquid.

**Solvent:** liquid that dissolves substances to form a solution.

**Sound:** vibration that travels through a medium (gases, liquids, and solids).

*Silicon becomes a **semiconductor** when certain impurities, such as boron, are added.*

**Spectrum:** arrangement of electromagnetic radiations, such as light, from shortest to longest wavelengths. The visible spectrum is the spread of colours formed when a beam of white light is split into its separate wavelengths by, for example, a prism.

**Streamlining:** shaping an object so that it travels with the least resistance, or drag, through the air or through water.

**Subatomic particle:** particle that is smaller than the atom, such as a proton or an electron.

**Sublimation:** change of state in which a solid turns into a gas without melting into a liquid first.

**Supernova:** explosion of a massive star that blasts most of its matter into space, leaving behind either a very dense body called a pulsar or a black hole.

**Supersonic:** travelling faster than the speed of sound.

**Surface tension:** force on the surface of a liquid that makes it behave as if it has a skin.

**Synthetics:** substances produced from chemicals, particularly from petrochemicals. Some synthetic products, such as synthetic rubber, are designed to imitate natural products.

**Temperature:** measure of how hot or how cold something is. Three main temperature scales are in use: Fahrenheit, Kelvin, and Celsius.

**Transducer:** device for converting non-electrical energy or signals (such as light or sound) into electrical signals, or the other way round. The microphone and loudspeaker are transducers.

**Transistor:** electronic device consisting of a "sandwich" of semiconductor materials. It can be used to amplify signals, or as a switch (as in computer circuits).

**Ultrasound:** sound with a frequency higher than the human ear can detect.

**Ultraviolet (UV) light:** invisible electromagnetic radiation with a shorter wavelength than the violet rays in the visible spectrum. UV rays in sunlight can burn skin.

**Vector quantity:** one that has both magnitude and direction, such as velocity.

**Velocity:** speed and direction of an object.

**Viscosity:** measure of how thick a liquid is, or how easily it flows.

**Wavelength:** distance between the crest of one wave (light, sound, water) and the next. Wavelength is related to frequency – a wave with a short wavelength has a high frequency, and one with a long wavelength has a low frequency.

**Weight:** force exerted on a body by gravity. The more mass the body has, the greater its weight.

**Weightlessness:** popular term for the near absence of gravity experienced in an orbiting spacecraft. *See Microgravity.*

**Work:** work is done when a force moves a body a certain distance. It is a measure of energy transferred from one system to another and, like energy, it is measured in joules.

*Velocity is demonstrated with a home-made rocket.*

**X-rays:** penetrating electromagnetic waves with wavelengths between those of gamma rays and ultraviolet rays.

**Zero-G:** alternative term for weightlessness.

# INDEX

# ACKNOWLEDGEMENTS

**Picture Credits**

The publisher would like to thank the following for their kind permission to reproduce their images:

Position key: c=centre, b=bottom, l=left, r=right, t=top, a=above

*Bryan And Cherry Alexander Photography:* 92cl.
*Sportsphoto:* Brian Bahr 73tr.
*Aquarius Library:* 117cr; Claudette Barius (SMPSP) 116tr; ILM 116cr, 117b.
*Blackpool Pleasure Beach:* 63tc, 75tr.
*Stevebloom.com Images:* 109br.
*Bridgeman Art Library, London / New York:* Private Collection – Church Interior by Abel Grimmer (1570-1619) 110cr.
*CERN:* 43cl.
*Corbis:* 3bc, 25bl, 35bl, 47cl, 70tr, 70br, 85cl, 93br, 94tr, 98cl, 100-101, 112bl, 127bl, 134bc, 145tl; Aaron Horowitz 70-71; Amos Nachoum 32tr; Bettmann Archive 79bl, 117c–background; Bill Ross 62tr; Gilbert Lundt; TempSport 57tl; James A. Sugar 70cl; Jay Dickman 119; NASA / Roger Ressmeyer 71bl; Neil Beer 56br; Owen Franken 71cr; Ralph White 32bl; Richard A. Cooke 77br; Rick Doyle 119br; Roger Ressmeyer 69tl.

*Steve Cross Partnership:* 137br.
*Denoyer-Geppert:* Intl. 94cr.
*Ecoscene:* 52cl.
*EDFA:* 74br.
*Empics Ltd:* 34b.
*Mary Evans Picture Library:* 88tr, 91cr.
*Eye Ubiquitous:* David Forman 95bl.
*Gables:* 62bl.
*Robert Harding Picture Library:* 34-35t, 37tl.
*Heritage Image Partnership:* Science Museum 80bl.
*Hibbert / Ralph:* 116-117t
*High Field Magnetic Laboratory, University of Nijmegen, the Netherlands:* 137bl.
*Hovertravel Limited:* 66bl.
*Robin Hunter:* 115bc
*The Image Bank / Getty Images:* 2clb, 30cr, 73tl, 81tr, 86tc; Frans Lemmens 74c; Kenneth Redding 14l; Leo Mason. Split Second 66-67c.
*ImageState:* 12br.
*BFI London Imax Cinema:* BFI London Imax Cinema 116br.
*Memoflex:* Memoflex from Aspex 13br.
*Museum of Moving Image:* 105bl1, 105bl2.
*N.A.S.A.:* 2tr, 46tr, 65tl, 112br, 119tl, 135br; Kennedy Space Centre 84cl.
*Stephen Oliver:* 36r, 136t.
*Oxford Scientific Films:* 114tl; Peter O'Toole 48br; Vinay Parelkar / Dinodia 56tr.
*Pictor International:* 71tl; Steve Vidler 70br.
*Brian Pitkin:* 25tl, 57bl.

*Powerstock Photolibrary / Zefa:* 2c, 76b.
*Rail Images:* 142b.
*Santa Pod Raceway:* 69cr.
*Science Museum:* 62br, 92br, 107tr, 108l, 109cr, 112cr, 113br, 114tl, 138cl, 141cl.
*Science Photo Library:* 2-3, 24tr, 26tr, 26cl, 31cl, 35tr, 36br, 37bl, 38-39, 41cr, 43cr, 43br, 44tr, 44cl, 44cr, 44bc, 44bc, 46cl, 46cr, 47tc, 47tr, 53tr, 54cl, 54br, 54-55b, 55tl, 57br, 64bl, 84br, 84-85, 85cb, 87bl, 87br, 88bl, 88br, 89cr, 90c, 91tl, 93tl, 96-97b, 97tl, 104cr, 105cr, 107cl, 107c, 107br, 108cr, 109bl, 112tl, 112tr, 113tl, 113c, 113bl, 114bc, 122-3, 124tr, 125br, 126br, 126r, 127tr, 129t, 131tr, 131b, 132tr, 132bl, 134-5, 138bl, 140bl, 142cl, 144tr, 144br, 145tr, 147tl, 147tr, 147br, 148cl, 148bc, 148-9c, 149br; A.B Dowsett 58tr; Adam Hart-Davis 14-15c, 75cl; Astrid & Hanns-Frieder Michler 14bl; Biophoto Associates 59cl; BSIP 14cr; Colin Cuthbert 51tl; Damien Lovegrove 110tr; David Nunuk 81br; Dr Gary Settles 82-83; Francoise Sauze 56c; Gary Ladd 32bc; I. Andersson, Oxford Molecular Biophysics Laboratory 16tc; J-L Charmet 67tr; James Bell 8-9; James Holmes 48c;

Jerrican Godfryd 33bl; Jerry Mason 48tr; Kent Wood 49b; L.Medard / Eurelios 41tl; Lawrence Berkeley 11tr; Lawrence Berkeley Laboratory 40bl; Manfred Kage 58-59c; Martin Bond 78tr; Mehau Kulyk 56l; NASA 19cb, 69cl; Pekka Parviainen 58b; Philippe Plailly 40tr; R. Maisonneuve 1011tc; Renee Lynn 18br; Richardson / Custom Medical Stock Photo 59br; Rosenfeld Images Ltd 50cl; Scott Camazine 59tl; Stephen Dalton 68cl; TRL LTD 64tl.
*Skyscan:* 70cl, 71c.
*Still Pictures:* 52b.
*Stone / Getty Images:* 26bl, 64tr, 75br, 79cl, 94bl, 99tr, 99cl; David Leah 60-61c; George Lepp 68-69b.
*Telegraph Colour Library / Getty Images:* 19br, 133br; Michael Dunning 11b; Phil Boorman 68cr.
*Art Directors & TRIP:* S. Grant 86cb.

All other images © Dorling Kindersley. For further information see:
**www.dkimages.com**
**Artworks:**
*Robin Hunter*
  20-21c, 25br, 30l, 34cl, 47b, 49tl, 55tr, 55br, 63br, 90bl, 95tl, 98r,

104tr, 106 cl, 107br, 110cra, 119cr, 127tl, 128cl, 130cl,114bl, 130br, 131tr, 136bl, 140tr, 140cl, 140cr, 142tr, 143tl, 144c, 145c.
*Martin Wilson*
  28tr, 28b.
*John Kelly*
  42b, 43t, 45.

**Dorling Kindersley would like to thank the following people for their contributions to the making of this book:**

Design assistance:
  Polly Appleton,
  Ann Cannings,
  Darren Holt,
  Clair Watson.
Editorial assistance:
  David John,
  Margaret Hynes.
Proof reading:
  Lee Simmons.
Lynn Bresler for the index;
Kate Bradshaw for hand modelling;
Roger Langston at King's College London, University of London, for kindly loaning scientific equipment;
Craig Outhwaite at Evans Cycles, The Cut, London SE1 for the loan of the bicycle for the "Gears and Pulleys" experiment on p. 78.